math expressions

Dr. Karen C. Fuson

Watch the sugar glider come alive in its tree-top world as you discover and solve math challenges.

Download the *Math Worlds AR* app available on Android or iOS devices.

Grade **5**

Volume 2

This material is based upon work supported by the
National Science Foundation
under Grant Numbers
ESI-9816320, REC-9806020, and RED-935373.

Any opinions, findings, and conclusions, or recommendations expressed in this material
are those of the author and do not necessarily reflect the views of the National Science Foundation.

BIG IDEA 1 - Length, Area, and Volume

BIG IDEA 2 - Liquid Volume, Mass, and Weight

BIG IDEA 3 - Attributes of Two-Dimensional Figures

BIG IDEA 4 - Perimeter and Area of Other Polygons

BIG IDEA 5 - Attributes of Three-Dimensional Figures

© Houghton Mifflin Harcourt Publishing Company

Student Resources

Dear Family:

The main goal of Unit 5 of *Math Expressions* is to enhance skills in dividing with whole numbers and decimal numbers. Some additional goals are:

- to solve real world application problems,
- to use patterns as an aid in calculating,
- to use estimation to check the reasonableness of answers, and
- to interpret remainders.

Your child will learn and practice methods such as the Place Value Sections Method, the Expanded Notation Method, and the Digit-by-Digit Method to gain speed and accuracy in multidigit and decimal division. Money examples will be used to help students understand division with decimals.

Throughout Unit 5, your child will solve real world application problems that require multidigit division. Your child will learn to estimate using rounding and other methods, and then to use estimation to determine whether answers are reasonable. Remainders will be interpreted in real world contexts, and expressed as fractions or decimals when appropriate. Students will learn to distinguish between multiplication and division in real world situations involving decimals.

If you have any questions, please contact me.

Sincerely,
Your child's teacher

Estimada familia:

El objetivo principal de la Unidad 5 de *Math Expressions* es reforzar las destrezas de división con números enteros y decimales. Algunos objetivos adicionales son:

- resolver problemas con aplicaciones a la vida diaria,
- usar patrones como ayuda para hacer cálculos,
- usar la estimación para comprobar si las respuestas son razonables, y por último,
- interpretar residuos.

Su niño aprenderá y practicará métodos como el Método de las Secciones de valor posicional, el Método de la Notación extendida y el Método de Dígito por dígito, para realizar divisiones de números de varios dígitos y decimales con mayor rapidez y exactitud. Como ayuda para comprender las divisiones con decimales, se usarán ejemplos de dinero.

En la Unidad 5 su niño resolverá problemas con aplicaciones a la vida diaria que requieran el uso de la división de números de varios dígitos. Aprenderá a estimar usando el redondeo y otros métodos, y luego usará la estimación para determinar si las respuestas son razonables. Los residuos se interpretarán dentro de contextos de la vida diaria y se expresarán como fracciones o decimales cuando sea apropiado. Los estudiantes aprenderán a distinguir entre la multiplicación y la división en situaciones de la vida cotidiana que involucren decimales.

Si tiene alguna duda o algún comentario, por favor comuníquese conmigo.

Atentamente,
El maestro de su niño

Divide Whole Numbers by One Digit

overestimate

remainder

underestimate

An estimate that is too big.

The number left over when a divisor does not divide evenly into a dividend.

Example:

$$\begin{array}{r} 13 \\ 7{\overline{\smash{\big)}\,94}} \\ \underline{-7} \\ 24 \\ \underline{21} \\ 3 \end{array}$$ ⟵ remainder

An estimate that is too small.

Name _____

Compare Division Methods

An airplane travels the same distance every day. It travels 3,822 miles in a week. How far does the airplane travel each day?

Rectangle Model

Place Value Sections Method

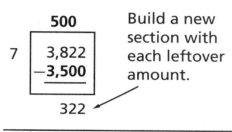

Build a new section with each leftover amount.

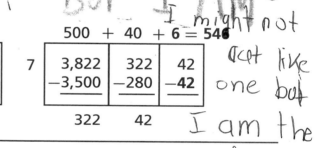

Expanded Notation Method

```
     500
  7)3,822
   -3,500
      322
```

Show the zeros in the multipliers.

```
      40
     500
  7)3,822
   -3,500
      322
     -280
       42
```

```
    6
   40 )546
  500
7)3,822
 -3,500
    322
   -280
     42
    -42
```

Digit-by-Digit Method

```
     5
  7)3,822
   -3,5
     32
```

Put in only one digit at a time.

```
     54
  7)3,822
   -35
     32
    -28
     42
```

```
    546
  7)3,822
   -3,5
     32
    -28
     42
    -42
```

Division Problems

Write an equation. Then solve.

Show your work.

1 A farmer has 2,106 cows and 9 barns. If the farmer divides the cows into equal groups, how many cows will he put in each barn?

_____

2 A sidewalk covers 3,372 square feet. If the sidewalk is 4 feet wide, what is its length?

?

4 ft | Area = 3,372 sq. ft

_____

3 Olivia has $8. Her mother has $4,784. The amount Olivia's mother has is how many times the amount Olivia has?

_____

4 A machine produced 4,650 bottles of seltzer and put them in packs of six bottles. How many 6-packs did the machine make?

_____

5 Raj is 3,288 days old. This is 6 times as old as his niece. How many days old is Raj's niece?

_____

6 If a streamer is unrolled, its area is 3,888 square inches. If the streamer is 2 inches wide, how long is it?

_____

Divide Whole Numbers by One Digit

Name

Work with Remainders

VOCABULARY
remainder

The problem at the right might seem unfinished. The leftover number at the bottom is called the remainder. We can write the answer like this: 567 R2.

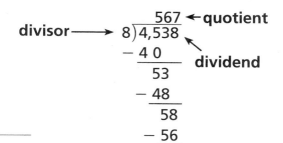

7 Could there be a remainder of 9 for the problem? Why or why not?

_____

_____

_____

8 What is the greatest possible remainder when dividing by 8?

_____

Complete each division and give the remainder.

9 $6\overline{)5,380}$ **10** $7\overline{)6,747}$ **11** $5\overline{)4,914}$

12 $5\overline{)2,428}$ **13** $3\overline{)2,972}$ **14** $7\overline{)4800}$

15 $9\overline{)5,469}$ **16** $4\overline{)3,183}$ **17** $6\overline{)5,420}$

Use Mental Math to Check for Reasonableness

Miguel has 6 boxes to store 1,350 baseball cards.
He divides and finds that each box will have 225 cards.
To check that his answer is reasonable, he uses
estimation and mental math:

$$\begin{array}{r} 225 \\ 6)\overline{1,350} \end{array}$$

"I know that 1,200 ÷ 6 is 200 and 1,800 ÷ 6 is 300.
Because 1,350 is between 1,200 and 1,800, my answer
should be between 200 and 300. It is."

Solve. Then use mental math to check the solution.

18 $9)\overline{3,150}$ **19** $3)\overline{2,733}$ **20** $6)\overline{4,560}$ **21** $8)\overline{7,136}$

22 Kim makes necklaces with colored beads. She used
1,620 beads for 9 necklaces. How many beads did she use
for each necklace if they have the same number of beads?

_____

23 Saul delivers equally 1,155 newspapers in a 7-day week.
How many newspapers does he deliver in a day?

_____

24 Val earns $1,096 a month as a cashier. She makes $8 an hour.
How many hours does she work in a month?

_____

25 The Martinson School bought 1,890 water bottles to distribute
equally among students over a 5-day period. How many bottles
are distributed each day?

_____

 Check Understanding
Describe and demonstrate a method for dividing a
multidigit number by a one-digit number.

Divide Whole Numbers by One Digit

Name _____

Experiment with Two-Digit Divisors

Suppose 2,048 sheep are to be sent on a train.
Each railroad car holds 32 sheep.

To find how many railroad cars are needed for the
sheep, divide 2,048 by 32.

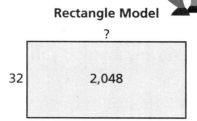

Rectangle Model

| 32 | 2,048 |

?

Discuss how these division methods are alike and different.

Digit-by-Digit

Step 1	Step 2	Step 3	Step 4
$32\overline{)2,048}$ (30)	$32\overline{)2,048}$ (30) top: 6	6; $32\overline{)2,048}$ (30) $-1\,92$; 128	64; $32\overline{)2,048}$ (30) $-1\,92$; 128 -128
Round the divisor.	Estimate the first digit: 30 divides into 200 about 6 times.	Multiply and subtract. Bring down 8 ones.	Estimate the next digit and multiply.

Expanded Notation

Step 1	Step 2	Step 3	Step 4
$32\overline{)2,048}$ (30)	60; $32\overline{)2,048}$ (30)	60; $32\overline{)2,048}$ (30) $-1,920$; 128	4 } 64; 60; $32\overline{)2,048}$ (30) $-1,920$; 128 -128
Round the divisor.	Estimate the first number: 30 divides into 2,000 about 60 times.	Multiply and subtract. $60 \cdot 32 = 1,920$	Estimate the next number and multiply.

Place Value Sections

Step 1	Step 2	Step 3	Step 4
60; 32 (30)	2,048		60; 32 (30)	2,048 $-1,920$	128	60 +; 32 (30)	2,048 $-1,920$	128	128	60 + 4; 32 (30)	2,048 $-1,920$	128	128 -128	0
Round the divisor and estimate the first number.	Multiply and subtract.	Make a new section.	Estimate the next number, and multiply and subtract.

Explore Dividing by Two-Digit Whole Numbers **213**

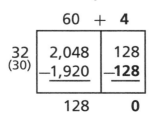

Experiment with Two-Digit Divisors (continued)

Look at Exercises 1–3. Would you round the divisor up or down to estimate the first digit of the quotient? Complete each exercise, using any method you choose.

1 $79 \overline{)4{,}032}$ **2** $21 \overline{)1{,}533}$ **3** $18 \overline{)1{,}061}$

Does Estimation Always Work?

Complete Exercise 4 as a class. Does rounding give you a correct estimate of the first digit? Does it give you a correct estimate of the next digit? Discuss what you can do to finish the problem.

4 $54 \overline{)3{,}509}$

Complete and discuss each exercise below. Use any method you choose.

5 $74 \overline{)3{,}651}$ **6** $42 \overline{)3{,}231}$ **7** $23 \overline{)1{,}892}$

✓ Check Understanding

Complete using *greater* or *lesser*. When an estimated digit in the quotient is too high, you should try a _____ digit.

Explore Dividing by Two-Digit Whole Numbers

Underestimating

VOCABULARY
overestimate
underestimate

Here are two ways to divide 5,185 ÷ 85. Discuss each method and answer the questions as a class.

$$\overset{\overset{(90)}{5}}{85\overline{)5,185}}$$
$$-\ 4\ 25$$
$$\overline{93} \longleftarrow \text{What does this number tell us?}$$

How do we know that the first estimated number is not right? What number should we try next? Solve the problem using that number.

$$\overset{\overset{\overset{10}{\ \ \ }}{50}}{\overset{(90)}{85\overline{)5,185}}} \longleftarrow \text{What does this number tell us?}$$
$$-\ 4,250$$
$$\overline{935}$$

How do we know that the first estimated number is not right this time? Do we need to erase, or can we just finish solving the problem? Try it.

1 When we estimate with a number that is too big (**overestimate**), we have to erase and change the number. When we estimate with a number that is too small (**underestimate**), do we always have to erase? Explain your answer.

_____

_____

_____

_____

Solve each division. You may need to adjust one or both of the estimated numbers.

2 $56\overline{)4,032}$

3 $77\overline{)4,791}$

4 $18\overline{)798}$

Too High or Too Low?

Think about what kind of divisor is most likely to lead to an estimated number that is wrong. Test your idea by doing the first step of each problem below.

5 $41\overline{)2{,}583}$ **6** $34\overline{)1{,}525}$ **7** $29\overline{)928}$ **8** $16\overline{)1{,}461}$

9 What kind of divisor is most likely to lead to an estimated number that is wrong? How can you adjust for these cases?

_____

_____

Mixed Practice with Adjusted Estimates

10 Hector is packing 1,375 oranges in crates that hold 24 oranges each.

How many crates will Hector fill? _____

How many oranges will be left over? _____

11 Skateboards sell for $76 each. This week the store sold $5,396 worth of skateboards.

How many skateboards were sold?

_____

12 Ashley's dog Tuffy eats 21 ounces of food for each meal. Ashley has 1,620 ounces of dog food.

How many meals will Tuffy have
before Ashley needs to buy more food? _____

How many ounces of food
will be left after the last meal? _____

 Check Understanding

If the estimate of the first digit of a quotient is too low, you

should try the next _____ digit.

Too Large, Too Small, or Just Right?

Decide What to Do with the Remainder

Think about each of these ways to use a remainder.

Sometimes you ignore the remainder.

1 A roll of ribbon is 1,780 inches long. It takes 1 yard of ribbon (36 inches) to wrap a gift.

How many gifts can be wrapped?

_____

Why do you ignore the remainder?

_____

_____

Sometimes you round up to the next whole number.

2 There are 247 people traveling to the basketball tournament by bus. Each bus holds 52 people.

How many buses will be needed?

_____

Why do you round up?

_____

_____

Sometimes you use the remainder to form a fraction.

3 The 28 students in Mrs. Colby's class will share 98 slices of pizza equally.

How many slices will each student get?

$$\begin{array}{r} 3\frac{1}{2} \\ 28\overline{)98} \\ -\ 84 \\ \hline 14 \end{array}$$

_____

Look at the division shown here. Explain how to get the fraction after you find the remainder.

_____

_____

Decide What to Do with the Remainder (continued)

Sometimes you use a decimal number instead of the remainder.

Suppose 16 friends earned $348 at a car wash. They want to divide the money equally. The division at the right shows that each friend gets $21, and there are $12 leftover. Dividing the $12, each friend gets an additional $\frac{12}{16}$, or $\frac{3}{4}$, of a dollar, for a total of $21.75.

$$
\begin{array}{r}
21.75 \\
16\overline{)348} \\
-32 \\
\hline
28 \\
-16 \\
\hline
12
\end{array}
$$

4 A rectangular garden has an area of 882 square meters. The long side of the garden has a length of 35 meters. How long is the short side?

_____

Sometimes the remainder is the answer to the problem.

5 A bagel shop has 138 bagels to be packed into boxes of 12 to be sold. The extra bagels are for the workers.

How many bagels will the workers get?

_____

Why is the remainder the answer?

_____

_____

Solve Problems Involving Remainders

Solve.   *Show your work.*

6 At the Cactus Flower Cafe, all tips are divided equally among the waiters. Last night, the 16 waiters took in $1,108 in tips. How much did each waiter get?

_____

7 A gardener needs to move 2,150 pounds of dirt. He can carry 98 pounds in his wheelbarrow. How many trips will he need to make with the wheelbarrow?

_____

Interpret Remainders

Name _____

Solve Problems Involving Remainders (continued)

Solve. *Show your work.*

8 Mia must work 133 hours during the month of May. There are 21 working days in May this year. How many hours per day will Mia work if she works the same number of hours each day?

_____

9 Colored markers cost 78 cents each. Pablo has $21.63 in his pocket. How many markers can Pablo buy?

_____

10 A meat packer has 180 kilograms of ground meat. He will divide it equally into 50 packages. How much will each package weigh?

_____

11 In volleyball, there are 12 players on the court. If 75 people all want to play volleyball at a gym that has more than enough courts, how many of them must sit out at one time?

_____

12 At the Fourth of July celebration, 1,408 ounces of lemonade will be shared equally by 88 people. How many ounces of lemonade will each person get?

_____

13 Armando needs quarters to ride the bus each day. He took $14.87 to the bank and asked to have it changed into quarters. How many quarters did he get?

_____

What's the Error?

Dear Math Students,

I am moving, and I need to pack my sardines.
I have 1,700 cans of sardines, and I know I can fit 48
cans in each box.

I divided to figure out how many boxes I needed.
I bought 35 boxes, but I had some cans leftover. What
did I do wrong?

Your friend,
Puzzled Penguin

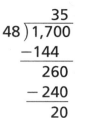

$$
\begin{array}{r}
35 \\
48\overline{)1{,}700} \\
-144 \\
\hline
260 \\
-240 \\
\hline
20
\end{array}
$$

14 Write a response to Puzzled Penguin.

_____

_____

_____

_____

_____

Write Your Own Problem

15 Write a word problem that involves a division that has
a remainder. Solve your problem and explain what
you did with the remainder in your solution.

_____

_____

_____

_____

✓**Check Understanding**

Explain how you decide what to do with a remainder
when you solve a word problem involving division.

Interpret Remainders

Name _____

Practice Dividing

Divide.

① 6)‾5‾4‾6‾

② 43)‾1‾,‾6‾3‾4‾

③ 5)‾4‾2‾3‾

④ 73)‾3‾,‾9‾4‾2‾

⑤ 5)‾7‾,‾0‾1‾6‾

⑥ 55)‾2‾,‾2‾0‾0‾

⑦ 13)‾9‾,‾4‾3‾0‾

⑧ 29)‾1‾,‾4‾9‾9‾

⑨ 3)‾4‾,‾0‾4‾0‾

⑩ 8)‾2‾,‾0‾0‾7‾

⑪ 88)‾6‾,‾1‾6‾0‾

⑫ 76)‾3‾,‾4‾4‾1‾

Solve Division Word Problems

Solve.   *Show your work.*

13 Thomas's rectangular backyard has an area of 2,352 square feet. If the yard is 56 feet long, how wide is it?

_____

14 Avocados are on sale for 84¢ each. How many avocados can Milo buy if he has $7.75?

_____

15 One quart is equal to 32 ounces. How many quarts are equal to 6,672 ounces?

_____

16 Students in the marching band sold calendars to raise money for new uniforms. Violet sold 24 calendars for a total of $186. How much did each calendar cost?

_____

17 37 fans came to the volleyball team's first match. At the last match, 2,035 fans came. The number of fans at the last match was how many times the number as the first?

_____

18 Ayala has 655 computer files she wants to put on thumb drives. If she can fit 18 files on each thumb drive, how many thumb drives will she need?

_____

19 Ms. Adams wrote a 36-page story. She buys a 500-sheet package of paper and prints as many copies of the story as she can. How many sheets does she have left over?

_____

✓ **Check Understanding**

Suppose Problem 18 asked "What is the greatest number of thumb drives Ayala can fill?" The answer would be _____ thumb drives.

Division Practice

Divide. Express remainders as whole numbers.

1. $9\overline{)841}$

2. $68\overline{)5,361}$

Write an equation. Then solve.

Show your work.

3. The workers at a company packaged 6,984 juice boxes into packs of 8. How many packs are there?

_____

Solve.

4. Sydney puts her coin collection into an album. She has 584 coins. If each page holds 12 coins, how many pages does Sydney need?

_____

5. A sports store owner has 2,860 basketballs he wants to donate to youth leagues. There are 82 leagues. If each league gets the same number of basketballs, how many basketballs will each league get? How many basketballs will be left over?

_____

Name _____ **Date** _____

Multiply.

1   20
    × 4

2   36
    × 3

3   500
    × 6

4   350
    × 4

5   804
    × 7

6   467
    × 9

7   419
    × 6

8 3,000
    ×   5

9 5,040
    ×   8

10 4,409
    ×   7

11 6,274
    ×   8

12   20
    × 40

13   63
    × 50

14   72
    × 19

15   87
    × 56

Name _____

Divide a Decimal by a One-Digit Number

Three friends set up a lemonade stand and made $20.25. They will share the money equally. Study the steps below to see how much money each person should get.

When the $20 is split 3 ways, each person gets $6. There is $2 left.	We change the $2 to 20 dimes and add the other 2 dimes. There are 22 dimes.	When we split 22 dimes 3 ways, each person gets 7 dimes. There is 1 dime left.	We change the dime to 10 cents and add the other 5 cents. Now we split 15 cents 3 ways.
$$\begin{array}{r} 6 \\ 3\overline{)20.25} \\ -18 \\ \hline 2 \end{array}$$	$$\begin{array}{r} 6. \\ 3\overline{)20.25} \\ -18 \\ \hline 2.2 \end{array}$$	$$\begin{array}{r} 6.7 \\ 3\overline{)20.25} \\ -18 \\ \hline 2.2 \\ -2.1 \\ \hline .1 \end{array}$$	$$\begin{array}{r} 6.75 \\ 3\overline{)20.25} \\ -18 \\ \hline 2.2 \\ -2.1 \\ \hline .15 \\ -.15 \end{array}$$

Divide.

1 $8\overline{)47.68}$ **2** $9\overline{)58.68}$ **3** $6\overline{)316.2}$ **4** $5\overline{)98.65}$

Write an equation. Then solve.

5 Imelda has 8.169 meters of rope. She wants to cut it into 3 equal pieces to make jump ropes for her 3 friends. How long will each jump rope be?

_____

6 Tonio has 7.47 pounds of rabbit food. He will divide it equally among his 9 rabbits. How much food will each rabbit get?

_____

Divide a Decimal by a Two-Digit Number

A company bought 38 sandwiches for a business meeting. Each sandwich costs the same amount. The sandwiches cost $161.12 in all. What was the price of each sandwich?

To answer this question, we have to divide the total price among the 38 sandwiches. We round the divisor, 38, up to 40 to estimate the multipliers.

When $161 is divided into 38 parts, each part is $4. There is $9 left.	We change the $9 to 90 dimes and add the other dime. There are 91 dimes.	When we split 91 dimes into 38 parts, each part is 2 dimes. There are 15 dimes left.	We change the 15 dimes to 150 pennies and add the other 2 pennies. Now we split 152 pennies 38 ways.
$$\begin{array}{r} {\scriptstyle(40)}\ \ 4 \\ 38\overline{)161.12} \\ -152 \\ \hline 9 \end{array}$$	$$\begin{array}{r} {\scriptstyle(40)}\ \ 4 \\ 38\overline{)161.12} \\ -152 \\ \hline 9.1 \end{array}$$	$$\begin{array}{r} {\scriptstyle(40)}\ \ 4.2 \\ 38\overline{)161.12} \\ -152 \\ \hline 9.1 \\ -7.6 \\ \hline 1.5 \end{array}$$	$$\begin{array}{r} {\scriptstyle(40)}\ \ 4.24 \\ 38\overline{)161.12} \\ -152 \\ \hline 9.1 \\ -7.6 \\ \hline 1.52 \\ -1.52 \end{array}$$

Divide.

7 $51\overline{)374.85}$ **8** $22\overline{)580.8}$ **9** $78\overline{)706.68}$ **10** $36\overline{)547.2}$

Write an equation. Then solve.

11 A rectangle has an area of 35.75 square meters and a length of 11 meters. What is its width?

_____

12 Katsu bought 18 pounds of apples for $23.04. What was the price for each pound?

_____

Divide Decimal Numbers by Whole Numbers

Name _____

Write Zeros at the End of the Dividend

Writing zeros at the end of a number, *after* the decimal point, does not change the value of the number. This idea can help us solve some division problems.

Eight friends bought movie tickets. The total cost for the tickets was $78. How much did each friend pay?

When the $78 is divided among 8 people, each person pays $9, and there is $6 still left to divide.	Write a decimal point and a 0. Bring down the 0 (trade $6 for 60 dimes) and continue to divide. Each person pays 7 dimes more, and there are 4 dimes left to divide.	Write another 0 after the decimal point. Bring down the 0 (trade 4 dimes for 40 pennies) and finish dividing. Each person pays 5 pennies more, for a total of $9.75.

$$\begin{array}{r} 9 \\ 8\overline{)78} \\ -72 \\ \hline 6 \end{array}$$

$$\begin{array}{r} 9.7 \\ 8\overline{)78.0} \\ -72 \\ \hline 6.0 \\ -5.6 \\ \hline .4 \end{array}$$

$$\begin{array}{r} 9.75 \\ 8\overline{)78.00} \\ -72 \\ \hline 6.0 \\ -5.6 \\ \hline .40 \\ -.40 \end{array}$$

13 Jun rode her bike to the bookstore and back. According to her bike's odometer, the round trip distance was 6.65 miles. She started the division at the right to figure out the one-way distance to the bookstore. Write a 0 at the end of the dividend and finish the division.

The distance to the bookstore is _____ miles.

$$\begin{array}{r} 3.32 \\ 2\overline{)6.65} \\ -6 \\ \hline 0.6 \\ -0.6 \\ \hline .05 \\ -.04 \\ \hline .01 \end{array}$$

Divide.

14 $6\overline{)54.75}$

15 $5\overline{)141.2}$

16 $8\overline{)310}$

Patterns in Division by Powers of 10

Recall that powers of 10, such as 10^1, 10^2, and 10^3 represent repeated multiplication with 10. The exponent tells you how many times to use 10 as a factor.

$10^1 = 10$ $10^2 = 10 \times 10 = 100$ $10^3 = 10 \times 10 \times 10 = 1{,}000$

Study the patterns in Exercises 18 and 19. Then complete Exercises 20–23.

18 $35.6 \div 10 = \underline{3.56}$

$35.6 \div 100 = \underline{0.356}$

$35.6 \div 1{,}000 = \underline{0.0356}$

19 $125 \div 10^1 = \underline{12.5}$

$125 \div 10^2 = \underline{1.25}$

$125 \div 10^3 = \underline{0.125}$

20 $50.7 \div 10^1 = \underline{\hspace{1cm}}$

$50.7 \div 10^2 = \underline{\hspace{1cm}}$

$50.7 \div 10^3 = \underline{\hspace{1cm}}$

21 $916.2 \div 10 = \underline{\hspace{1cm}}$

$916.2 \div 100 = \underline{\hspace{1cm}}$

$916.2 \div 1{,}000 = \underline{\hspace{1cm}}$

22 $4{,}076 \div 10^1 = \underline{\hspace{1cm}}$

$4{,}076 \div 10^2 = \underline{\hspace{1cm}}$

$4{,}076 \div 10^3 = \underline{\hspace{1cm}}$

23 $7.8 \div 10^1 = \underline{\hspace{1cm}}$

$7.8 \div 10^2 = \underline{\hspace{1cm}}$

$7.8 \div 10^3 = \underline{\hspace{1cm}}$

24 Complete these statements to summarize your work in Exercises 18–23.

a. Dividing a number by 10^1, or 10, shifts the digits to the right _____ place(s).

b. Dividing a number by 10^2, or 100, shifts the digits to the right _____ place(s).

c. Dividing a number by 10^3, or 1,000, shifts the digits to the right _____ place(s).

Patterns Relating Multiplication and Division

Use the multiplication problem to help you solve the division problem.

25 $32 \div 8 = \underline{\hspace{1cm}}$

$8 \times \underline{\hspace{1cm}} = 32$

26 $3.2 \div 8 = \underline{\hspace{1cm}}$

$8 \times \underline{\hspace{1cm}} = 3.2$

27 $0.32 \div 8 = \underline{\hspace{1cm}}$

$8 \times \underline{\hspace{1cm}} = 0.32$

28 $0.032 \div 8 = \underline{\hspace{1cm}}$

$8 \times \underline{\hspace{1cm}} = 0.032$

Check Understanding

Divide.

$5.8 \div 5 = \underline{\hspace{1cm}}$

$0.15 \div 3 = \underline{\hspace{1cm}}$

$9.6 \div 12 = \underline{\hspace{1cm}}$

Divide Decimal Numbers by Whole Numbers

Name _____

Use Money to See Shift Patterns

Jordan earns $243 a week. The money is shown here

Jordan's Earnings in Dollars

$ ____ ____ ____   2   4   3

| ÷ 1 |

| $243 ÷ 1 = $243 |

Answer each question about how much Jordan earns in coins.

1 How many dimes ($0.10) does he earn?

_____

2 What happens to each dollar? Why?

_____

_____

3 What happens to the number showing Jordan's earnings? Why?

_____

_____

4 When you divide by 0.1, does each digit shift right or left? Why?

_____

_____

5 How many places does each digit shift? Why?

_____

_____

Jordan's Earnings in Dimes

____ ____ 2 , 4   3   0

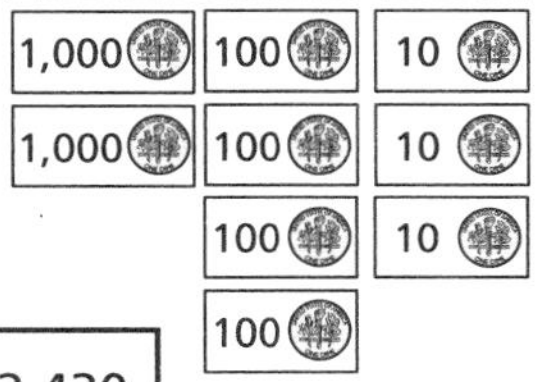

1,000	100	10
1,000	100	10
	100	10
	100	

| ÷ 0.1 |

| 243 ÷ 0.1 = 2,430 |

Use Money to See Shift Patterns (continued)

6 How many pennies ($0.01) does he earn?

_____

7 What happens to each dollar?

_____

8 What happens to the number showing Jordan's earnings?

_____

9 When you divide by 0.01, does each digit shift right or left? Why?

_____

10 How many places does each digit shift? Why?

_____

_____

Jordan's Earnings in Pennies

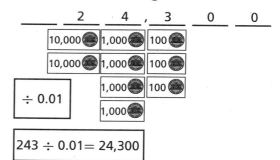

$$243 \div 0.01 = 24,300$$

11 How many tenths of a cent ($0.001) does he earn?

_____

12 What happens to each dollar?

_____

13 What happens to the number showing Jordan's earnings? Why?

_____

14 When you divide by 0.001, does each digit shift right or left? Why?

_____

15 How many places does each digit shift? Why?

_____

Jordan's Earnings in Tenths of a Cent

2	4	3 ,	0	0	0
100,000	10,000	1,000			
100,000	10,000	1,000			
	10,000	1,000			
	10,000				

$\div 0.001$

$$243 \div 0.001 = 243,000$$

Divide Whole Numbers by Decimal Numbers

Relate Decimal Division to Multiplication

Solve.   *Show your work.*

16 Mrs. Moreno made 1 liter of grape jelly. She will put it into jars that each hold 0.1 liter. How many jars will she need?

Think: How many tenths are there in 1 whole? _____

Complete the equation: $1 \div 0.1 =$ _____.

This answer is the same as $1 \times$ _____.

17 Mr. Moreno made 2 liters of juice. He will pour it into glasses that each hold 0.1 liter. How many glasses will he need?

Think: How many tenths are there in 1 whole? _____

How many tenths are there in 2 wholes? _____

Complete the equation: $2 \div 0.1 =$ _____.

This answer is the same as $2 \times$ _____.

18 The Morenos made a kiloliter of fruit punch for a large party. They will pour it into punch bowls that each hold 0.01 kiloliter. How many bowls will they need?

Think: How many hundredths are there in 1 whole? _____

Complete the equation: $1 \div 0.01 =$ _____.

This answer is the same as $1 \times$ _____.

19 When we divide a number by a decimal number less than one, why is the quotient greater than the original number?

_____

_____

_____

_____

What's the Error?

Dear Math Students,

I was absent today. My friend told me we learned to divide by 0.1 and 0.01. She said that when you divide by 0.1, the digits shift one place, and when you divide by 0.01, they shift two places. Here are two problems from my homework.

$45 \div 0.1 = 4.5$ $45 \div 0.01 = 0.45$

Are my answers correct? If not, can you explain what I did wrong?

Your friend,
Puzzled Penguin

20 Write a response to the Puzzled Penguin.

_____

_____

_____

_____

Change Decimal Divisors to Whole Numbers

You can use the strategy below to change a division problem with a decimal divisor to an equivalent problem with a whole number divisor.

Discuss each step used to find 6 ÷ 0.2.

Step 1: Write 6 ÷ 0.2 as a fraction.

$$6 \div 0.2 = \frac{6}{0.2}$$

Step 2: Make an equivalent fraction with a whole number divisor by multiplying $\frac{6}{0.2}$ by 1 in the form of $\frac{10}{10}$. Now you can divide 60 by 2.

$$\frac{6}{0.2} \times 1 = \frac{6}{0.2} \times \frac{10}{10} = \frac{60}{2}$$

21 Why is the answer to 60 ÷ 2 the same as the answer to 6 ÷ 0.2?

_____

_____

_____

Divide Whole Numbers by Decimal Numbers

Name _____

Change Decimal Divisors to Whole Numbers (continued)

You can use the strategy of multiplying both numbers by 10 even when a division problem is given in long division format.

Step 1: Put a decimal point after the whole number.

Step 2: Multiply both numbers by 10, which shifts the digits one place left. Show this by making curved arrows to show the decimal points. Write zeros if necessary.

$$0.2\overline{)6.}$$

$$0.2\overline{)6.0.}$$

Step 3: Instead of drawing arrows, you can make little marks called carets (^) to show where you put the "new" decimal points. Now divide 60 by 2.

$$0.2_\wedge\overline{)\overset{3\,0.}{6.0_\wedge}}$$

22 Why does making both numbers 10 times as large give us the same answer?

_____

_____

Answer each question to describe how to find 6 ÷ 0.02 and 6 ÷ 0.002.

23 Suppose you want to find 6 ÷ 0.02.

By what number can you multiply 0.02 to get a whole number? _____

Describe and show how to use curved arrows to show an equivalent division and solve.

$$0.02\overline{)6.}$$

_____

24 Suppose you want to find 6 ÷ 0.002.

By what number can you multiply 0.002 to get a whole number? _____

Describe and show how to use curved arrows to show an equivalent division and solve 6 ÷ 0.002.

$$0.002\overline{)6.}$$

_____

Practice Dividing by Decimals

Divide.

25 $0.5\overline{)45}$ **26** $0.07\overline{)56}$ **27** $0.8\overline{)496}$ **28** $0.65\overline{)910}$

29 $0.12\overline{)60}$ **30** $0.004\overline{)16}$ **31** $0.9\overline{)468}$ **32** $0.75\overline{)270}$

33 $0.3\overline{)96}$ **34** $0.06\overline{)42}$ **35** $0.072\overline{)216}$ **36** $2.4\overline{)192}$

Solve.   *Show your work.*

37 A dime weighs about 0.08 ounce. About how many dimes weigh a pound (16 ounces)?

_____

38 A quarter weighs about 0.2 ounce. About how many quarters weigh 2 pounds (32 ounces)?

_____

39 A dime is about 0.14 centimeter thick. Zeynep made a stack of dimes 35 centimeters high. About how many dimes did she use?

_____

40 A newborn mouse weighs about 0.25 ounce. A newborn cat weighs about 4 ounces. A newborn cat weighs how many times as much as a newborn mouse?

_____

✔ **Check Understanding**

To find the quotient for the problem 98 ÷ 0.34, I multiply the divisor and the dividend by _____ . The equivalent problem is _____ ÷ _____ .

Name _____

Use Money to See Shift Patterns

It costs $0.312 (31 cents and $\frac{2}{10}$ cent) to make one Cat's Eye
Marble. The money is shown here.

Cost of a Cat's Eye Marble

$ ____ ____ 0 . 3 1 2 ____

÷ 1

$0.312 ÷ 1 = $0.312

Answer each question about the different coins.

1 How many dimes ($0.10) does it cost to make
one Cat's Eye Marble?

_____

____ ____ 3 . 1 2 ____
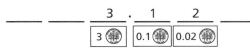

÷ 0.1

0.312 ÷ 0.1 = 3.12

2 What happens to the number that shows
the cost?

_____

_____

3 When you divide by 0.1, does each digit shift to
the right or left? Why?

_____

_____

_____

4 How many places does each digit shift? Why?

_____

_____

_____

Use Money to See Shift Patterns (continued)

5 How many pennies ($0.01) does it cost to make one Cat's Eye Marble?

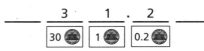

$$\underline{\quad} \; \underline{3} \; \underline{1} \; . \; \underline{2} \; \underline{\quad} \; \underline{\quad}$$

÷ 0.01

6 What happens to the number that shows the cost?

$$0.312 \div 0.01 = 31.2$$

7 When you divide by 0.01, does each digit shift to the right or left? Why?

8 How many places does each digit shift? Why?

9 How many tenths of a cent ($0.001) does it cost to make one Cat's Eye Marble?

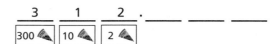

$$\underline{3} \; \underline{1} \; \underline{2} \; . \; \underline{\quad} \; \underline{\quad} \; \underline{\quad}$$

÷ 0.001

10 What happens to the number that shows the cost?

$$0.312 \div 0.001 = 312$$

11 When you divide by 0.001, does each digit shift to the right or left? How many places? Why?

12 Are the shift patterns for dividing by 0.1, 0.01, and 0.001 the same when the product (dividend) is a decimal number as when the product (dividend) is a whole number? Why or why not?

Divide a Decimal Number by a Decimal Number

Name _____

Change Decimal Divisors to Whole Numbers

To divide a decimal by a decimal, use the same strategy
you used when you divided a whole number by a decimal.

Discuss each step used to find 0.06 ÷ 0.2.

Step 1: Write 0.06 ÷ 0.2 as a fraction.

$$0.06 \div 0.2 = \frac{0.06}{0.2}$$

Step 2: Make an equivalent fraction
with a whole number divisor by
multiplying $\frac{0.06}{0.2}$ by 1 in the form
of $\frac{10}{10}$. Now divide 0.6 by 2.

$$\frac{0.06}{0.2} \times 1 = \frac{0.06}{0.2} \times \frac{10}{10} = \frac{0.6}{2}$$

13 Why does 0.06 ÷ 0.2 have the same answer as 0.6 ÷ 2?

_____

_____

_____

_____

**Here are the steps for using the strategy when the problem
is in long division form.**

Step 1: Set up the problem.

$$0.2\overline{)0.06}$$

Step 2: Multiply both numbers by 10. This shifts
the digits one place left. Show this by
moving the decimal point one place right.

$$0.2{\scriptstyle\wedge}\overline{)0.0{\scriptstyle\wedge}6}$$

Step 3: You don't have to draw arrows. Carets (^)
show where each "new" decimal point
belongs. Now divide 0.6 by 2.

$$0.2{\scriptstyle\wedge}\overline{)0.0{\scriptstyle\wedge}6}$$ with $.3$ as quotient

14 Why does moving the digits the same number
of places give a problem with the same answer
as the original problem?

_____

_____

_____

Change Decimal Divisors to Whole Numbers (continued)

15 How would you find 0.06 ÷ 0.02 with long division? What number do you need to multiply both numbers by to make 0.02 a whole number?

$0.02 \overline{)0.06}$

_____

_____

16 How would you find 0.06 ÷ 0.002 with long division? What number do you need to multiply both numbers by to make 0.002 a whole number?

$0.002 \overline{)0.06}$

_____

_____

Divide. Show your work.

17 $0.9 \overline{)7.2}$　　　**18** $0.04 \overline{)0.364}$　　　**19** $0.6 \overline{)0.372}$　　　**20** $0.14 \overline{)7.28}$

Write an equation. Then solve.

21 A developer is building an amusement park on a rectangular lot with an area of 1.35 square miles. The length of one side of the lot is 0.45 mile. What is the length of the other side?

0.45 mi | Area = 1.35 sq. mi | ?

_____

✓ **Check Understanding**

Draw a place value chart and use it to show how the digits for dividing a decimal by a decimal shift for both the divisor and the dividend.

Name _____

Divide Mentally

Use the fact that 1,715 ÷ 35 = 49 to solve each problem.

① $35\overline{)17.15}$ **②** $35\overline{)171.5}$ **③** $0.35\overline{)0.1715}$ **④** $35\overline{)17{,}150}$

⑤ $3.5\overline{)1{,}715}$ **⑥** $0.35\overline{)1{,}715}$ **⑦** $3.5\overline{)17.15}$ **⑧** $0.35\overline{)1.715}$

Solve Division Problems

Divide. If both numbers are whole numbers, give your answer as a whole number with a remainder.

⑨ $0.6\overline{)54}$ **⑩** $0.08\overline{)72}$ **⑪** $0.5\overline{)0.45}$ **⑫** $0.07\overline{)0.49}$

⑬ $0.05\overline{)34.5}$ **⑭** $7\overline{)395}$ **⑮** $0.045\overline{)41.85}$ **⑯** $42\overline{)4{,}009}$

⑰ $0.02\overline{)98.8}$ **⑱** $6\overline{)980}$ **⑲** $0.04\overline{)117}$ **⑳** $0.081\overline{)64.881}$

Check for Reasonable Answers

Solve. Check that your answer is reasonable.

Show your work.

21 Clark is having a party. He has 196 chairs, and wants to put 8 chairs at each table. How many chairs will be left over?

_____

22 Liam needs to buy 640 eggs for a soccer breakfast. If eggs come in cartons of 18, how many cartons should he buy?

_____

23 Jacob made $507 this year. If he makes the same amount monthly, how much money did he make each month?

_____

24 Johna made a rectangular sign. The area of the sign is 7 square meters, and its length is 4 meters. What is the width of the sign?

_____

25 Lakisha and Raj went to an electronics store. Lakisha bought a television for $358.40. This is 28 times as much as Raj spent on a new video game. How much did Raj's video game cost?

_____

26 Kyle spent $27.28 on cookies for a party. Each cookie cost 44 cents ($0.44). How many cookies did Kyle buy?

_____

✓ **Check Understanding**

What expression could you use to check to see if your answer to $52 \div 0.43$ was reasonable?

_____

Division Practice

Name _____

Multiply or Divide?

Read the problem. Then answer the questions.

1 A turtle walks 0.2 mile in 1 hour. How far can it walk in 0.5 hour?

    a. Do you need to multiply or divide to solve? _____

    b. Will the answer be more or less than 0.2 mile? _____

    c. What is the answer? _____

2 Gus ran 3.6 miles. He took a sip of water every 0.9 mile. How many sips did he take?

    a. Do you need to multiply or divide to solve? _____

    b. Will the answer be greater or less than 3.6? _____

    c. What is the answer? _____

3 Last year 135 cows on Dixie's Dairy Farm had calves. This year 0.6 times that many cows had calves. How many cows had calves this year?

    a. Do you need to multiply or divide to solve? _____

    b. Will the answer be greater or less than 135? _____

    c. What is the answer? _____

4 A box contains 1.2 pounds of cereal. A serving weighs 0.08 pound. How many servings are in the box?

    a. Do you need to multiply or divide to solve? _____

    b. Will the answer be greater or less than 1.2? _____

    c. What is the answer? _____

5 A rectangular patio has an area of 131.52 square meters. The width of the patio is 9.6 meters. What is its length?

    a. Do you need to multiply or divide to solve? _____

    b. Will the answer be greater or less than 131.52 meters? _____

    c. What is the answer? _____

Results of Whole Number and Decimal Operations

Answer each question.

6 If a and b are whole numbers greater than 1, will $b \times a$ be greater than or less than a? Why?

_____

_____

7 If a is a whole number and d is a decimal less than 1, will $d \times a$ be greater than or less than a? Why?

_____

_____

8 If a and b are whole numbers greater than 1, will $a \div b$ be greater than or less than a? Why?

_____

_____

_____

9 If a is a whole number and d is a decimal less than 1, will $a \div d$ be greater than or less than a? Why?

_____

_____

_____

Use reasoning to compare the expressions. Write $>$, $<$, or $=$.
Do not compute the actual values.

10 $42 \times 356 \bigcirc 356 \div 42$

11 $0.65 \times 561 \bigcirc 561 \div 0.65$

12 $832 \div 67 \bigcirc 832 \div 0.67$

13 $738 \times 66 \bigcirc 738 \times 0.66$

14 $126 \div 0.9 \bigcirc 126 \times 0.9$

15 $3{,}500 \times 0.7 \bigcirc 3{,}500 \times 7$

16 $64 \times 0.64 \bigcirc 64 \div 0.64$

17 $5{,}602 \div 42 \bigcirc 5{,}602 \div 0.42$

Distinguish Between Multiplication and Division

Name _____

Make Predictions

Solve.   *Show your work.*

18 Farmer Ortigoza has 124.6 acres of land. Farmer Ruben has 0.8 times as much land as Farmer Ortigoza.

   a. Does Farmer Ruben have more or less than 124.6 acres?

   _____

   b. How many acres does Farmer Ruben have? _____

19 Mee Young has 48 meters of crepe paper. She will cut it into strips that are each 0.6 meter long.

   a. Will Mee Young get more or fewer than 48 strips?

   _____

   b. How many strips will Mee Young get? _____

20 Jenn's garden is a rectangle with length 3.5 meters and width 0.75 meters.

   a. Is the area of the garden greater or less than 3.5 square meters?

   _____

   b. What is the area of the garden? _____

21 Roberto can lift 103.5 pounds. That is 0.9 times the amount his friend Vance can lift.

   a. Can Vance lift more or less than 103.5 pounds?

   _____

   b. How many pounds can Vance lift? _____

22 The Daisy Cafe served 18 liters of hot chocolate today. Each serving was in a cup that held 0.2 liter.

   a. Did the cafe serve more or fewer than 18 cups of hot chocolate?

   _____

   b. How many cups did the cafe serve? _____

Mixed Practice

Solve. Check your work.

23 $6\overline{)5.1}$ **24** $34\overline{)1.564}$ **25** $0.8\overline{)7.52}$ **26** $0.96\overline{)460.8}$

27 $\begin{array}{r} 0.4 \\ \times\ 0.8 \\ \hline \end{array}$ **28** $\begin{array}{r} 0.35 \\ \times\ 94 \\ \hline \end{array}$ **29** $\begin{array}{r} 0.37 \\ \times\ 0.09 \\ \hline \end{array}$ **30** $\begin{array}{r} 4.29 \\ \times\ 0.27 \\ \hline \end{array}$

Mixed Real World Applications

Solve. Check that your answer is reasonable.

Show your work.

31 Polly bought 12 beach balls for her beach party. She spent $23.64. How much did each beach ball cost?

_____

32 The 245 fifth graders are going on a trip. Each van can carry 16 students. How many vans will be needed for the trip?

_____

33 Today Aaliyah ran 4.5 miles per hour for three fourths (0.75) of an hour. How far did Aaliyah run today?

_____

✔ **Check Understanding**

Make the statements true by using > or <.

$a \cdot 0.3 \bigcirc a$ $a \div 0.3 \bigcirc a$

     Distinguish Between Multiplication and Division

Name _____

Math and Currency

When you travel from one country to another, you sometimes need to exchange your currency for the currency used in the country you are visiting. An exchange rate is the rate at which one currency can be exchanged for another.

Currencies are usually compared to 1 U.S. dollar (1 USD) when they are exchanged. For example, 1 USD may be exchanged for 6.7 Chinese yuans or 1.32 Canadian dollars. The exact amount of the exchange often varies from day to day.

Solve.

Show your work.

1 Suppose 5 U.S. dollars (5 USD) can be exchanged for 42 Norwegian kroner. What operation would be used to find the value of 1 USD in kroner?

_____

Find the value of 1 USD in kroner. 1 USD = _____ kroner

Math and Currency (continued)

Complete the exchange rate column of the table.   *Show your work.*

Country	Currency Unit	Equivalent Amounts	Exchange Rate
② Japan	yen	20 USD = 2,048 yen	1 USD = _____ yen
③ England	pound	10 USD = 7.7 pounds	1 USD = _____ pound(s)
④ Germany	euro	50 USD = 45 euros	1 USD = _____ euro(s)

Visiting another country often means exchanging more than 1 USD for the currency of that country.

⑤ The exchange rate for francs, the currency of Switzerland, is 10 USD = 9.6 francs. At that rate, how many francs would be exchanged for 25 USD?

_____

⑥ A traveler in Latvia exchanged 5 USD for 3.1 lats. At that rate, what is the cost of a souvenir in lats if the cost is 3 USD?

_____

⑦ A tourist would like to exchange 100 USD for kuna, the currency of Croatia. At the rate 12 USD = 80.4 kuna, how many kuna should the tourist receive?

_____

⑧ The cost to visit a famous tourist attraction in Russia is 812.5 rubles. What is the cost in USD if the exchange rate is 3 USD = 195 rubles?

_____

Name ______________________ Date ______________

Divide.

Show your work.

1. $0.04\overline{)23.6}$

2. $3\overline{)22.5}$

3. $0.7\overline{)1.61}$

Solve.

4. A rectangular door sign has an area of 577.6 square centimeters. The length of the sign is 38 centimeters. What is its width?

____

5. Charlie bought a skateboard for $98.91. This is 3 times as much as the cost of the helmet he bought. What is the cost of the helmet?

____

Name _____ **Date** _____

Multiply.

1   47
    × 3

2   29
    × 5

3   600
    × 4

4   810
    × 9

5   903
    × 5

6   297
    × 4

7   529
    × 7

8   5,000
    ×   8

9   3,007
    ×   6

10   5,036
    ×   8

11   3,784
    ×   7

12   30
    × 30

13   88
    × 40

14   76
    × 65

15   93
    × 87

1 Select the expression that involves a shift of the digits to the right 2 places. Mark all that apply.

(A) $9 \div 1{,}000$ (B) $30 \div 10^2$ (C) $2 \div 10^3$

(D) $7 \div 10$ (E) $400 \div 10^1$ (F) $8 \div 100$

2 Classify each quotient as being equal to 52, equal to 5.2, or equal to 0.52. Write the letter of the quotient in the correct box.

A $52 \div 10^2$ B $52 \div 10^1$ C $520 \div 10^1$

D $520 \div 10^2$ E $520 \div 10^3$ F $5{,}200 \div 10^3$

52	5.2	0.52

3 Explain why $0.04\overline{)3.6}$ has the same answer as $4\overline{)360}$.

4 Why does dividing 5 by a decimal less than 1 give a quotient greater than 5?

5 A farmer ships 4 times as many oranges as tangerines. The farmer ships 8,260 oranges. How many tangerines does he ship? Write an equation. Then solve.

6 Jamal buys postcards of Washington, D.C., for $10.20, not including tax. Each postcard costs $0.85. How many postcards does Jamal buy?

_____ postcards

7 Paige's backyard has an area of 95.9 square meters. The length of the yard is 14 meters. What is its width?

14 m

Area = 95.9 m² | ?

_____ meters

8 Mr. Adams divides 223 markers equally among the 26 students in his class. He puts the extra markers in a box. What is the least number of markers he puts in the box?

_____ markers

9 A park creates new habitats for 182 monkeys. Each habitat will house 8 or fewer monkeys.

Part A

What is the least number of habitats the zoo will need?

_____ habitats

Part B

What did you do with the remainder? Explain why.

10 Solve. Express the remainder as a whole number. Show your work. Draw a model to show how you solved the problem.

$57\overline{)970}$

11 Circle the word or phrase that makes the sentence true.

When you divide by 100, each digit shifts

to the | right / left | by | one place / two places / three places | .

12 Select each quotient that is correct. Mark all that apply.

Ⓐ $300 \div 100 = 3$

Ⓑ $3 \div 10 = 0.03$

Ⓒ $27 \div 100 = 0.27$

Ⓓ $60 \div 10 = 600$

13 Fill in the table to complete the pattern of dividing by powers of ten.

$4.72 \div 0.1$	4.72×10	_____
$4.72 \div 0.01$	$4.72 \times$ _____	472
$4.72 \div$ _____	$4.72 \times 1{,}000$	_____

14 Solve. $2{,}412 \div 3$. Explain how you know your answer is reasonable.

15 Nina is putting equal amounts of oatmeal into 4 containers. She has 37.6 ounces of oatmeal. How many ounces of oatmeal should she put into each container?

_____ ounces

16 Select each quotient equal to 0.28. Mark all that apply.

(A) $2.8 \div 10^2$

(B) $28 \div 10^3$

(C) $280 \div 10^3$

(D) $2.8 \div 10^1$

(E) $28 \div 10^1$

17 Lunch for the band costs $137.20. The band has 56 members. How much does each member's lunch cost?

$ _____

18 Marco got a quotient of 70 when he divided 49 by 0.07.

Part A

What is the correct answer for this problem?

Part B

What mistake did Marco make?

19 Write the letter of the expression next to the number that shows its quotient.

A $845 \div 27$ ☐ 31 R4

B $190 \div 6$ ☐ 24 R10

C $612 \div 15$ ☐ 31 R8

D $363 \div 9$ ☐ 24 R9

E $298 \div 12$ ☐ 40 R12

F $441 \div 18$ ☐ 40 R3

20 James lives 3.42 kilometers from school. Megan lives 0.76 kilometer from school. The distance James lives from school is how many times as long as the distance Megan lives from school? Show your work.

21 Fill in the table to complete the pattern of dividing by powers of ten.

$36 \div 10^1$	$36 \div 10$	_____
$36 \div 10^2$	$36 \div$ _____	0.36
$36 \div 10^{—}$	$36 \div 1{,}000$	_____

22 For numbers 22a–22c, read the word problem and circle the phrase from the box that makes the sentence correct.

22a. In a movie, 289 aliens plan to visit Earth. Each ship can hold as many as 3 aliens. What is the least number of ships needed?

For the remainder in this problem, you should | ignore it / round it up / form a fraction with it .

22b. Basma cuts ribbon to tie onto balloons for the carnival. She has 925.6 inches of ribbon in all. If each ribbon must be 24 inches long, how many ribbons can she cut?

For the remainder in this problem, you should | ignore it / round it up / form a fraction with it .

22c. Six miners divide 15 ounces of gold dust equally. How many ounces of gold dust does each miner receive?

For the remainder in this problem, you should | ignore it / round it up / form a fraction with it .

23 Write the correct number in each box in the place value sections to find the quotient.

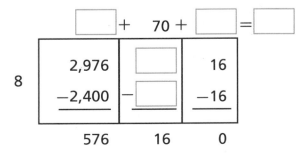

$$\boxed{} + 70 + \boxed{} = \boxed{}$$

8	2,976 −2,400	$\boxed{}$ −$\boxed{}$	16 −16
	576	16	0

Test Your Memory!

Susie keeps her music, book, and video collections on her computer. She sometimes downloads items to her tablet computer to take with her when she travels. She has 15 gigabytes of free space on her tablet. This table shows the average storage requirements for the media files Susie has.

Media Type	Average Size
Books	1 MB
TV Shows	0.5 GB
Movies	1.2 GB
Songs	6 MB

1 One gigabyte (GB) is equal to 1,000 megabytes (MB). Find the size of one book and one song in gigabytes. Then find the size of one TV show and one movie in megabytes. Explain how you can use mental math to solve the problem.

_____

_____

_____

_____

2 Susie's books take up 0.4 gigabyte of space and her songs take up 9,000 megabytes of space on her computer. How many books and songs does Susie have?

_____

_____

3 Susie thinks that a book is 2 times the size of a TV show. Is she correct? If not, explain her mistake.

_____

_____

_____

4 Susie can download 5 megabytes of data per second. How many minutes would it take to download 4 movies? Show your work.

5 Not all of Susie's files will fit on her tablet. She decides to divide the available space equally for each type of media file. Is this a good plan? Justify your answer.

6 Suppose Susie always keeps 2 GB of photos and 8 GB of songs on her tablet. Give two combinations of movies, books, and TV shows that she can download onto her tablet. Which combination leaves more space remaining on the tablet?

7 Now Susie has only 50 MB of free space on her tablet. She wants to purchase a game that takes up 800 MB of space. What combination gives the fewest items she can remove to make space available for her new game? Explain how you solved the problem.

Dear Family:

In Unit 6 of *Math Expressions*, your child will apply the skills the class has learned about operations with fractions, whole numbers, and decimals as they solve real world problems involving addition, subtraction, multiplication, and division.

A *situation equation* shows the structure of the information in a problem. A *solution equation* shows the operation that can be used to solve a problem. Your child will review situation and solution equations for addition and subtraction, and for multiplication and division. These methods of representing problems are particularly helpful when problems involve larger numbers that students cannot add, subtract, multiply, or divide mentally.

Your child will also solve multiplication and addition comparison problems and compare those types of problems, identifying how they are the same and how they are different.

Addition Comparison Problem

Terrell has 144 soccer trading cards. Manuel has 3 more cards than Terrell. How many cards does Manuel have?

Multiplication Comparison Problem

Elena has 74 stamps in her collection. Hassan has 3 times as many stamps. How many stamps does Hassan have?

Students learn that in the addition problem, they are adding 3, and multiplying by 3 in the multiplication problem.

Solving multistep problems is an important Grade 5 skill. Your child begins by solving one-step problems, then moves to two-step problems, and finally solves multistep problems which involve more than two steps. Your child will represent and use visual models and equations to find solutions for these problems.

Sincerely,
Your child's teacher

Estimada familia:

En la Unidad 6 de *Math Expressions*, su niño aplicará las destrezas que ha aprendido acerca de operaciones con fracciones, y números enteros y decimales, para resolver problemas de la vida cotidiana que involucren suma, resta, multiplicación y división.

Una *ecuación de situación* muestra la estructura de la información en un problema. Una *ecuación de solución* muestra la operación que se puede usar para resolver el problema. Su niño repasará ecuaciones de situación y de solución para suma y resta, y para multiplicación y división. Estos métodos de representar problemas son particularmente útiles cuando los problemas involucran números grandes que los estudiantes no pueden sumar, restar, multiplicar ni dividir mentalmente.

Su niño también resolverá problemas de comparación con multiplicación y con suma, y comparará ese tipo de problemas, identificando sus diferencias y semejanzas.

Problema de comparación con suma

Terrell tiene 144 tarjetas coleccionables de fútbol. Manuel tiene 3 tarjetas más. ¿Cuántas tarjetas tiene Manuel?

Problema de comparación con multiplicación

Elena tiene 74 estampillas en su colección. Hassan tiene el triple de estampillas. ¿Cuántas estampillas tiene Hassan?

Los estudiantes deben notar que en el problema con suma, suman 3 y en el problema con multiplicación multiplican por 3.

Resolver problemas de varios pasos es una destreza importante del 5.° grado. Su niño comenzará resolviendo problemas de un paso, luego de dos y finalmente resolverá problemas de varios pasos que tengan más de dos pasos. Usará modelos visuales y ecuaciones para representar y solucionar esos problemas.

Atentamente,
El maestro su niño

additive
comparison

multiplicative
comparison

A comparison in which one quantity is an amount greater or less than another. An additive comparison can be represented by an addition equation or a subtraction equation.

Example:

Josh has 5 more goldfish than Tia.

$j = t + 5$

$j - 5 = t$

A comparison in which one quantity is a number of times the size of another. A multiplicative comparison can be represented by a multiplication equation or a division equation.

Example:

Tomás picked 3 times as many apples as Catie.

$t = 3 \cdot c$

$t \div 3 = c$ or $\frac{1}{3} \cdot t = c$

Name _____

Write Equations to Solve Problems

A situation equation shows the structure of the information in a problem. A solution equation shows the operation that can be used to solve a problem.

Read the problem and answer the questions.

1 Last night, 312 people attended the early showing of a theater movie. How many people attended the late showing if the total attendance for both showings was 961 people?

a. The number of people who attended the first showing is known. Write the number.

_____

b. Write a situation equation to represent the problem. Use the letter n to represent the unknown number of people.

_____

c. Write a solution equation to solve the problem.

_____

d. Solve your equation.

_____

Write an equation to solve the problem. Draw a model if you need to.

Show your work.

2 A shopper spent $53.50 for a sweater and a T-shirt. What was the cost of the sweater if the cost of the T-shirt was $16.50?

_____

3 Jalen had $4\frac{2}{3}$ pounds of modeling clay and used $3\frac{1}{2}$ pounds for a craft project. How many pounds of clay were not used? When possible, express your answer with a whole or mixed number.

_____

4 Deborah drove 105.9 miles after stopping to rest. How many miles did she drive before the stop if she drove 231.7 miles altogether?

_____

Practice

Write an equation and use it to solve the problem.
Draw a model if you need to.

5 A car odometer showed 6,437.5 miles at the end of a trip. How many miles did the odometer show at the beginning of the trip if the car was driven 422.3 miles?

_____

6 Enrique has two packages to mail. The weight of one package is $12\frac{1}{4}$ pounds. What is the weight of the second package if the total weight of the packages is $15\frac{1}{8}$ pounds? If possible, express your answer with a whole or mixed number.

_____

Reasonable Answers

Use your reasoning skills to complete Problems 7 and 8.

7 Suppose you were asked to add the decimals at the right, and you wrote 2.07 as your answer. Without using pencil and paper to actually add the decimals, give a reason why an answer of 2.07 is not reasonable.

$$\begin{array}{r} 2.65 \\ + \ 0.42 \\ \hline \end{array}$$

_____

_____

8 Suppose you were asked to subtract the fractions at the right, and you wrote $\frac{5}{6}$ as your answer. Without using pencil and paper to actually subtract the fractions, give a reason why an answer of $\frac{5}{6}$ is not reasonable.

$\frac{1}{2} - \frac{1}{3}$

_____

_____

✔ **Check Understanding**

Explain what situation and solution equations are, and explain the relationship that addition and subtraction share in those equations.

Situation and Solution Equations for Addition and Subtraction

Name _____

Write Equations to Solve Problems

Sometimes it is helpful to write a situation equation and a solution equation to solve a problem. Other times you may write only a solution equation.

Read the problem and answer the questions.

① On the first day of soccer practice, $\frac{2}{5}$ of the players were wearing new shoes. The team has 20 players. How many players were wearing new shoes?

20

| $\frac{2}{5}$ | n |

a. The number of players wearing new shoes is given as a fraction. Write the fraction.

_____

b. The number of players on the whole team is given. Write the number.

_____

c. You are being asked to find a fraction of a whole. Write a solution equation to represent this fact.

_____

d. Solve your equation.

_____

Write an equation to solve the problem. Draw a model if you need to.

Show your work.

② The musicians in a marching band are arranged in equal rows, with 8 musicians in each row. Altogether, the band has 104 musicians. In how many rows are the musicians marching?

_____

③ Elena has chosen carpet that costs \$4.55 per square foot for a rectangular floor that measures $12\frac{1}{2}$ feet by $14\frac{1}{2}$ feet. How many square feet of carpet is needed to cover the floor?

_____

Practice

**Write an equation or equations and use it to solve the problem.
Draw a model if you need to.**

4 How many individual pieces of cheese, each weighing $\frac{1}{4}$ lb,
can be cut from a block of cheese weighing 5 pounds?

_____

5 A supermarket owner's cost for a 26-ounce can of coffee
is \$6.75. A case of coffee contains 12 cans. What profit is
earned for each case sold if each can sells for \$9.49?

_____

Reasonable Answers

Use your reasoning skills to complete Problems 6 and 7.

6 Suppose you were asked to multiply the numbers at the
right. Without actually multiplying the numbers, give a
reason why an answer of 15,000 is not reasonable.

$2{,}500 \times 0.6$

_____

_____

_____

7 Suppose you were asked to divide the numbers at the right.
Without actually dividing the numbers, give a reason why an
answer of 30 is not reasonable.

$90 \div \frac{1}{3}$

_____

_____

_____

✓ Check Understanding

Draw a Break Apart Model for $\frac{2}{5} + \frac{1}{5} = \frac{3}{5}$.

Draw a Rectangle Model for $n \cdot \frac{4}{7} = 20$.

Situation and Solution Equations for Multiplication and Division

Name _____

Write Multiplication Word Problems

Write a word problem for the equation.
Draw a model to show the situation. Solve the
word problem.

Show your work.

1 $\frac{3}{4} \cdot 2 = c$

_____

_____

_____

_____

2 $\frac{5}{6} \cdot s = \frac{5}{18}$

_____

_____

_____

_____

3 $\$6 \cdot 3.5 = d$

_____

_____

_____

_____

Write Division Word Problems

Write a word problem for the equation. Draw a model to show the situation. Solve the word problem.

Show your work.

4 $\frac{1}{4} \div c = \frac{1}{8}$

_____

_____

_____

_____

5 $s \div \frac{1}{2} = 6$

_____

_____

_____

_____

6 $\$16.50 \div 3 = r$

_____

_____

_____

_____

✓ **Check Understanding**

On a separate piece of paper, write a word problem for the equation $\frac{3}{4} \div 2 = \frac{3}{8}$ and one for the equation $\frac{3}{4} \cdot 2 = \frac{3}{2}$. Discuss how they are the same and how they are different.

Write Word Problems

Name _____

Use Rounding to Determine Reasonableness

**Write an equation and use it to solve the problem.
Use rounding to show that your answer is reasonable.**

Show your work.

1 Altogether, 91,292 people live in Waterloo and Muscatine, two cities in Iowa. The population of Waterloo is 68,406 people. What is the population of Muscatine?

Equation and answer: _____

Estimate: _____

_____

2 Vernon spent $229.06 for groceries, and paid for his purchase with five $50 bills. What amount of change should he have received?

Equation and answer: _____

Estimate: _____

_____

Use Estimation and Mental Math to Determine Reasonableness

Write an equation to solve the problem. Use estimation and mental math to show that your answer is reasonable.

3 In a school gymnasium, 588 students were seated for an assembly in 21 equal rows. What number of students were seated in each row?

Equation and answer: _____

Estimate: _____

_____

4 To get ready for her first semester of school, Jayna spent a total of $7.92 for eight identical notebooks. What was the cost of each notebook?

Equation and answer: _____

Estimate: _____

_____

Use Benchmark Fractions to Determine Reasonableness

Write an equation and use it to solve the problem. When possible, express your answer with a whole or mixed number. Use benchmark fractions to verify that your answer is reasonable.

5 A $\frac{5}{8}$-inch thick paperback book is placed on top of a $\frac{15}{16}$-inch thick paperback book. What is the total thickness of books?

Equation and answer: _____

Estimate: _____

_____

6 A cabinetmaker cut $\frac{7}{16}$ inch off a board that was $2\frac{7}{8}$ inches long. What is the new length of the board?

Equation and answer: _____

Estimate: _____

_____

Predict to Check for Reasonableness

Write an equation and use it to solve the problem. Use mental math to identify two whole numbers your answer should be between.

7 Four runners competed in a 10-kilometer relay race. Each runner ran the same distance. What was that distance?

Equation and answer: _____

Estimate: _____

_____

Check Understanding

Use the benchmark fractions 0, $\frac{1}{2}$, and 1 to estimate

$\frac{7}{8} + \frac{3}{7}$. Estimate: _____

Estimate $425 + 613$ by rounding each addend to the

nearest 100. Estimate: _____

Determine Reasonable Answers

Write an equation and use it to solve the problem.

Show your work.

1 Ethel is packing two suitcases for her vacation. The first suitcase weighs $24\frac{1}{2}$ pounds. The total weight of the suitcases is $49\frac{3}{4}$ pounds. What is the weight of the second suitcase?

_____

2 An airplane has 7 seats in each row. When the plane is full, it holds 175 passengers. How many rows of seats are there?

_____

Write a word problem for the equation.

3 $\frac{1}{4} \div f = \frac{1}{12}$

_____

_____

_____

Solve. Explain how you know your answer is reasonable.

4 Selma went shopping and bought identical sweaters for each of 3 friends. If she spent $42, what was the cost of each sweater?

_____

_____

5 Rico spent $5.70 on each of 8 toy cars. How much did he spend?

_____

_____

Name _____ Date _____

Multiply.

1.
```
  32
×  2
```

2.
```
  459
×   7
```

3.
```
  307
×   5
```

4.
```
  700
×   8
```

5.
```
  6,523
×     6
```

6.
```
  4,507
×     5
```

7.
```
  8,006
×     8
```

8.
```
  6,000
×     4
```

9.
```
   30
× 30
```

10.
```
  67
× 40
```

11.
```
  75
× 59
```

12.
```
  32
× 15
```

13.
```
  48
× 34
```

14.
```
  66
× 41
```

15.
```
  73
× 69
```

Name _____

The Jump Rope Contest

In comparison problems, you compare two amounts by addition or by multiplication. Draw comparison bars when needed.

Solve.   *Show your work.*

1. Julia jumped 1,200 times. Samantha jumped 1,100 times. How many more times did Julia jump?

   _____

2. Ahanu jumped 1,050 times. Rolando jumped 1,080 times. How many fewer times did Ahanu jump than Rolando?

   _____

3. Altogether the Blue Team jumped 11,485 times. The Red Team jumped 827 more times than the Blue Team. How many times did the Red Team jump?

   _____

4. Altogether the Green Team jumped 10,264 times. The Yellow Team jumped 759 fewer times than the Green Team. How many times did the Yellow Team jump?

   _____

5. Ted jumped 1,300 times. He jumped 100 more times than Mario. How many times did Mario jump?

   _____

6. Isaac jumped 987 times. Carlos needs to do 195 more jumps to tie with Isaac. How many times has Carlos jumped so far?

   _____

7. Altogether the fourth graders jumped 345,127 times. If the fifth graders jumped 2,905 fewer jumps, there would have been a tie. How many times did the fifth graders jump?

   _____

Comparison Problems

Solve each comparison problem. *Show your work.*

8 Ty scored 6 points in the basketball game. Ed scored 4 times as many points as Ty. How many points did Ed score?

9 Ramon scored 10 points at the volleyball game. That was 5 times as many as David scored. How many points did David score?
(Hint: Did David score more or fewer points than Ramon?)

10 Ana has $15 in the bank. Her sister Benita has $\frac{1}{3}$ as much money in the bank. How much money does Benita have in the bank?

11 Dana has 9 files of music downloads. She has $\frac{1}{5}$ as many as Sonya. How many files of music downloads does Sonya have?

12 Chester has 49 files of music downloads. Tony has $\frac{1}{7}$ as many as Chester. How many files of music downloads does Tony have?

13 A restaurant offers 18 types of pizza. A small cafe offers $\frac{1}{3}$ as many types of pizza. How many fewer types of pizza does the small cafe offer?

✓**Check Understanding**

Draw comparison bars to model the following problem and solve it.

Bill has 32 horses on his farm. He has 4 times as many horses as Joe. How many horses does Joe have?

Language of Comparison Problems

Name _____

Model and Solve Comparison Problems

The model below represents the time a student worked on spelling (**s**) and math (**m**) homework. Use the model for Problems 1–3.

Spelling | s |

Math | : : : : : : |

m

① Write a comparison sentence that includes the words "as long as" and compares

   a. *m* to *s*. _____

   b. *s* to *m*. _____

② Write a comparison equation that compares

   a. *m* to *s*. _____

   b. *s* to *m*. _____

③ Write a division equation that compares *s* to *m*.

_____

Solve. Draw a model if you need to.

④ The length of an unstretched spring is 120 cm. How long (*l*) will the spring be if it is stretched to 3 times that length?

_____

⑤ The length of a collapsed length fishing pole is *c*, which is $\frac{1}{8}$ times as long as its extended length. The extended length of the pole is 16 feet. What is its collapsed length?

_____

Multiplicative Comparison Situations **271**

Multiplication and Scaling

You can predict how resizing one factor will affect a product.

Solve.

6 Gina and Mario each receive a weekly allowance.
So far this year, Gina has saved $20 and Mario has saved
0.4 times that amount. Who has saved the greater amount
of money? Multiply to check your prediction.

Prediction: _____

7 Last week Camila worked 40 hours. Sergio worked $\frac{4}{5}$ that
length of time. Which person worked more hours last week?

Prediction: _____

8 On a math quiz, Juan was asked to find these two products:

$$3 \times 10.6 \qquad 2.7 \times 10.6$$

a. Without using pencil and paper to actually find
the products, how will the product of 3×10.6 compare
to the product of 2.7×10.6? Explain your answer.

_____

b. How will the product of 2.7×10.6 compare to the
product of 3×10.6? Explain your answer.

_____

9 How does the value of a fraction change when both the numerator
and the denominator of the fraction are multiplied by the same
number? Explain. Include an example to support your explanation.

_____

_____

_____

_____

✓ **Check Understanding**

If $n > 0$, circle the expression below with the greatest value.

$$n \cdot 2 \qquad n \cdot \frac{1}{2} \qquad n \cdot \frac{4}{4}$$

© Houghton Mifflin Harcourt Publishing Company

Multiplicative Comparison Situations

Solve Comparison Problems

For each problem, draw a model and write *additive comparison* or *multiplicative comparison* to identify the type of comparison. Then write and solve an equation to solve the problem.

1 Newborn baby Lila is 44.5 cm tall. Her older brother Tremaine is 4 times as tall. How tall (*t*) is Tremaine?

Show your model here.

Type of comparison: _____

Equation and answer: _____

2 Al has $\frac{1}{4}$ cup of flour, and needs $1\frac{5}{8}$ cups of flour. How many more cups (*c*) of flour does he need? Answer with a whole or mixed number.

Type of comparison: _____

Equation and answer: _____

3 Imani completed a 200-meter race in 25.06 seconds. Talia completed the same race in 1.17 fewer seconds. How long (*s*) did it take Talia to complete the race?

Type of comparison: _____

Equation and answer: _____

4 A high school has 1,446 students enrolled. A middle school has $\frac{1}{6}$ as many students enrolled as the high school. How many students (*m*) are enrolled in the middle school?

Type of comparison: _____

Equation and answer: _____

Practice

**Write an equation and use it to solve the problem.
Draw a model if you need to.**

Show your work.

5 At the time of the 2010 Ohio census, 155,416 more people
lived in Cincinnati than lived in Dayton. How many people (*p*)
lived in Dayton if 296,943 people lived in Cincinnati?

_____

6 A woodworking machine decreased the thickness of a board
from $\frac{3}{4}$ of an inch to $\frac{9}{16}$ of an inch. By what number of inches (*i*)
did the thickness of the board decrease?

_____

7 Tyler has saved $14.25 of his allowance. He would like to buy a
computer game that costs $15.70 more than the amount he has
saved. What is the cost (*c*) of the game?

_____

8 To prepare for a test, Esmeralda studied for 40 minutes.
Mallory studied for 50 minutes. How many times (*t*) as
long as Mallory did Esmeralda study?

_____

9 A flagpole has a height of 3.2 meters. A nearby tree has a
height of 25.6 meters. When compared to the flagpole, how
many times as tall (*t*) is the tree?

_____

10 A school fundraiser collected $776. Sun-Woo's class collected
$\frac{1}{16}$ of that amount. What amount of money (*m*) was collected
by Sun-Woo's class?

_____

✓ **Check Understanding**

In an additive comparison problem, you _____ or _____
to find the unknown amount. In a multiplicative comparison problem,

you _____ or _____ to find the unknown amount.

Types of Comparison Problems

Write the correct answer.

Show your work.

1 Toby spent 40 minutes studying for the spelling test. Sara studied 3 times as long as Toby. How long did Sara study for the spelling test?

_____

2 Maria has 48 markers. Sia has $\frac{1}{3}$ as many markers as Maria. How many markers does Sia have?

_____

3 A rattlesnake is 6 feet long. A python is 24 feet long. The python is how many times as long as the rattlesnake?

_____

4 Jaime made $35.47 less in the afternoon than in the morning. He made $95.24 in the morning. How much did he make in the afternoon?

_____

5 Kent is $39\frac{1}{2}$ inches tall. His sister Laurie is $21\frac{1}{5}$ inches tall. How much taller is Kent than Laurie?

_____

Name   Date

Multiply.

1   23
       × 3

2   219
        × 6

3   840
        × 3

4   200
        × 6

5   5,319
        ×   4

6   7,043
        ×   8

7   4,909
       ×   6

8   8,000
       ×   3

9   70
        ×20

10   53
        ×60

11   76
        ×32

12   41
        ×27

13   52
        ×28

14   79
        ×58

15   94
        ×78

Name _____

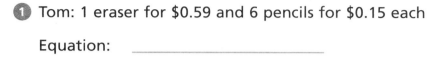

Write Equations

Write and solve an equation to find the amount of money each student spent at the school bookstore.

Show your work.

1 Tom: 1 eraser for $0.59 and 6 pencils for $0.15 each

Equation: _____

Answer: _____

2 Jay: 8 book covers for $0.90 each and 1 pen for $0.49

Equation: _____

Answer: _____

3 Joe: 12 notebooks for $1.75 each and 1 marker for $1.59

Equation: _____

Answer: _____

4 Bo: 1 pen for $2.50 and 6 portfolios for $1.25 each

Equation: _____

Answer: _____

5 Todd: 3 watercolor brushes for $2.39 each and a pencil sharpener for $0.89

Equation: _____

Answer: _____

Solve Equations With Parentheses

On another piece of paper, solve each equation. Write the answer here.

6 $(5 \cdot 60) - 2 = n$ $n =$ _____

7 $2.5 + (4 \div 0.1) = b$ $b =$ _____

8 $3 \cdot \left(1\frac{1}{2} - \frac{1}{8}\right) = z$ $z =$ _____

9 $\left(2 \div \frac{1}{4}\right) - 1 = v$ $v =$ _____

10 $\left(1\frac{3}{4} \div 3\right) + \frac{1}{4} = c$ $c =$ _____

11 $10 + \left(\frac{2}{3} \cdot 6\right) = h$ $h =$ _____

12 $1.55 - (0.7 \cdot 2) = r$ $r =$ _____

13 $(0.01 \cdot 100) - 1 = w$ $w =$ _____

Solve Two-Step Word Problems

Solve.   *Show your work.*

14 A suburban shopping mall has 105 rows of parking
spaces with 45 spaces in each row. A special permit is
required to park in 630 of those spaces. How many
spaces (s) do not require a special permit?

Equation: _____   Answer: _____

15 A recipe that makes 6 servings requires $1\frac{1}{4}$ cups of flour.
How much flour (f) would be needed to make the recipe
for one-half the number of servings?

Equation: _____   Answer: _____

16 An apple orchard in Minnesota has 8 rows of 26 honeycrisp
trees and 14 rows of 23 red delicious trees. How many
honeycrisp and red delicious trees (t) are in the orchard?

Equation: _____   Answer: _____

17 An investor purchased 250 shares of stock. Calculate the
investor's total cost (c) if the price per share was $18.40
and a fee of $65.75 was charged for the transaction.

Equation: _____   Answer: _____

18 An orange grove in Florida has 865 ambersweet trees and
32 rows of 40 sunstar trees. How many more (m) sunstar
than ambersweet trees does the orchard have?

Equation: _____   Answer: _____

19 A manufacturing facility records the time its employees
work each week in fractions of an hour.

Taliyah W. $25\frac{1}{2}$ hr   Avery S. $7\frac{3}{4}$ hr   Claire N. $39\frac{1}{4}$ hr

How many more hours (h) did Claire work than the combined
hours of Taliyah and Avery?

Equation: _____   Answer: _____

Equations and Parentheses

Name _____

Too Much or Too Little Information

Solve each problem if possible. If a problem has too much information, identify the extra information. If a problem has too little information, describe the information that is needed to solve the problem.

Show your work.

Meiling is reading a 228-page book. Yesterday she read the first 41 pages of the book. Today she read the next 13 pages. Her goal tomorrow is to read 10 pages. How many pages of the book have not been read as of today?

20 What information is not needed to solve the problem?

_____

21 Write the information that is needed to solve the problem. Then solve the problem.

_____

_____

The students in Mr. Westgate's class have been arranged in equal groups for an activity. There are four students in each group.

22 How many students are participating in the activity?

_____

To prepare for a math test, Kelsey studied for $\frac{1}{2}$ hr, Lila studied for $\frac{3}{4}$ hr, Ricardo studied for $\frac{1}{3}$ hr, and Marcus studied for 1 hour. Did Marcus study longer than the combined times of Ricardo and Kelsey?

23 What information is not needed to solve the problem?

_____

24 Write the information that is needed to solve the problem. Then solve the problem and explain your answer.

_____

_____

_____

Practice Problem Solving

Solve each problem if possible. If a problem has too much information, circle the extra information. If a problem has too little information, describe the information that is needed to solve the problem.

25 A wallpaper border is being pasted on the walls of a rectangular room that measures 12 feet by $14\frac{1}{2}$ feet. The cost of the border is $6.50 per foot. How many feet of border is needed for the room?

_____

_____

26 Ms. Bleyleven has 11 windows in her house. The heights in centimeters of 4 windows are 160.2 cm, 163 cm, 155.9 cm, and 158.5 cm. How many windows in her house have a height that is a whole number of centimeters?

_____

_____

27 Anja has worked at her job for $6\frac{1}{2}$ years. Each year she works 48 weeks, and each week she works $37\frac{1}{2}$ hours. How many hours does Anja work each year?

_____

_____

28 During a driving vacation, a car was refueled 5 times. At the beginning of the vacation, the car odometer read 19,417 miles, and read 21,068 miles at the end of the vacation. How many gallons of fuel were needed to drive that number of miles?

_____

_____

✓ **Check Understanding**

What is the total cost (c) of an $0.89 notebook and 8 pencils that cost $0.15 each? Write a situation equation and solve the problem.

_____

Equations and Parentheses

Solve Multistep Problems

Solve.

Show your work.

1 An investor purchased 150 shares of stock at $13.60 per share, and sold the shares later for $11.92 per share. Calculate the profit or loss of the transaction.

   a. What equation can be used to find the amount of money needed to buy (*b*) the shares?

   _____

   b. What equation can be used to find the amount of money received for selling (*s*) the shares?

   _____

   c. Does the transaction represent a profit or loss? Why?

   _____

   d. What equation can be used to calculate the loss (*l*)? Solve your equation to calculate the loss.

   _____

2 A soccer team plays 10 games each season. Last season the team scored an average of 2.5 goals per game in its first six games, and 3.25 goals per game in its final four games. How many goals (*g*) were scored by the team last season?

   _____

3 The charge for an automobile repair was $328.50 for parts and $64 per hour for labor. The repair took $3\frac{3}{4}$ hours. What was the total cost (*c*) of the repair?

   _____

4 An auditorium has 215 rows of seats with 35 seats in each row. A reservation is required to sit in the first 6 seats of 75 rows. How many seats (*s*) do not require a reservation?

   _____

Solve Multistep Problems (continued)

Show your work.

Solve.

5 At the school bookstore, Dakota purchased a notebook for $3.75, 6 pencils for $0.20 each, and 2 pens for $1.19 each. By what amount (*a*) was cost of the pens greater than the cost of the pencils?

_____

6 This week an employee is scheduled to work $7\frac{1}{2}$ hours each day Monday through Friday, and 2 hours on Saturday morning. If the employee's goal is to work 40 hours, how many additional hours (*h*) must be worked?

_____

7 Ryan went shopping and purchased two shirts for $16 each, and a pair of sneakers that cost $2\frac{1}{2}$ times as much as a shirt. What amount of money (*m*) did Ryan spend?

_____

8 At home last night, Reza spent 35 minutes doing homework, which is 10 more minutes than Colette. Katerina worked twice as long as Colette, but 5 fewer minutes than Orvis. How long (*l*) did Orvis spend doing homework last night?

_____

9 There is a line of 55 adults and 89 students waiting to ride a roller coaster. The coaster can hold 38 riders. How many trips (*t*) are needed to give everyone in line a ride? How many people will be on the last trip of the day?

_____

 Check Understanding

Will solving the equation below result in the correct answer for Problem 9? Write *yes* or *no*.

$38 \div (55 + 89) = t$ $\qquad$ $38(55 + 89) = t$ $\qquad$ $(55 + 89) \div 38 = t$

_____ $\qquad$ _____ $\qquad$ _____

Name _____

Practice Problem Solving

Solve each problem.

Show your work.

① Four college roommates drove 1,050 miles to Florida for spring break. Xavier drove 300 more miles than Yuri, and Yuri drove 200 more miles than Zack, who drove 60 miles. How many miles did Walter (w) drive?

   a. How many miles did Zack drive? _____

   b. What expression represents the miles Yuri drove? _____

   c. What expression represents the miles Xavier drove? _____

   d. The number of miles Walter drove (w) is the number of miles Zack, Yuri, and Xavier drove subtracted from the number of miles the friends drove altogether. Write an equation to represent this fact.

   _____

   e. How many miles did Walter drive? _____

② Sasha earns $8 per hour working at her grandparents' farm. During July, she worked $39\frac{1}{2}$ hours at the farm, and earned $47 babysitting. How many more dollars (d) does Sasha need to earn to buy a gadget that costs $399?

   _____

③ Anya, Jose, Cali, and Stephan walk for exercise. Anya's route is $2\frac{1}{4}$ kilometers long. Jose's route is $1\frac{1}{2}$ fewer kilometers than Anya's. Cali's route is $1\frac{1}{2}$ times as long as Jose's route, and 2 fewer kilometers than Stephan's route. What distance (d) is Stephan's route? If possible, answer with a whole or mixed number.

   _____

④ A $750 gift was shared equally by 5 people. After spending $90 of her share, Clarissa divided the amount remaining into 2 equal parts. What amount of money (p) does each part represent?

   _____

Solve each problem.

Show your work.

5 Chloe purchased a sweater that cost $24, and a shirt that cost $\frac{5}{8}$ times as much as the sweater. What amount of change (*c*) did Chloe receive if she gave the clerk $50?

_____

6 Six teachers, 78 students, and 10 parents are boarding buses for a school field trip. Each bus can carry 32 passengers. If the passengers board each bus until it is full, how many passengers (*p*) will be on the bus that is not full?

_____

What's the Error?

Dear Math Students,

I was asked to find the amount of change (*c*) a shopper would receive from $40 after purchasing a pair of jeans for $28 and a pair of socks that cost $\frac{1}{4}$ as much as the jeans. I used the solution equation $c = 40 - 28 - (28 \div \frac{1}{4})$ to solve the problem.

Can you tell me what I did wrong?

Your friend,
Puzzled Penguin

7 Write a response to Puzzled Penguin.

_____

_____

_____

 Check Understanding

In Problem 5, what does the expression $\frac{5}{8} \cdot 24$ represent? What does the expression $50 - 24$ represent?

Practice Problem Solving

Math and Gymnastics

In a gymnastics competition, gymnasts compete in events such as the balance beam, parallel bars, vault, and floor exercise.

Leigh earned the following scores from the judges for her balance beam routine.

9.20　　　9.30　　　9.20　　　9.30　　　9.20　　　9.00

Follow these steps to find Leigh's final score.

1 Order the scores from least to greatest.

_____

2 Cross off the lowest score and the highest score.

_____

3 Find the average of the remaining scores by adding the scores and dividing the sum by 4.

_____

4 Calculate Leigh's final score by adding 7.0 (the difficulty rating of her routine) to the average you found in Exercise 3.

_____

The judges' scores for Olivia's balance beam routine are shown below.

9.40　　　9.40　　　9.50　　　9.50　　　9.40　　　9.40

5 Calculate Olivia's average score by following the steps described in Exercises 1–3 above.

_____

_____

6 Calculate Olivia's final score by adding 6.6 (the difficulty of her routine) to the average you found in Exercise 5.

_____

Math and Diving

In diving competitions, divers compete in springboard and platform events.

Follow these steps to find the total score for a dive.

▸ Order the judges' scores from least to greatest.

▸ Cross off the lowest score and the highest score.

▸ Find the sum of the remaining scores.

▸ Multiply the sum by the difficulty of the dive.

7 Suppose a diver earned the following scores from judges on his first of five platform dives.

9.5   10.0   9.0   10.0   10.0

a. In the space at the right, sketch a bar graph to display the scores.

b. The difficulty of the dive was 3.8. Follow the steps above to calculate the total score for the dive.

_____

8 The table below shows the scores the diver received from the judges for his four remaining dives.

Dive	Scores					Difficulty
2	9.4	8.9	9.0	9.5	9.4	3.2
3	8.8	8.6	8.0	8.0	8.5	3.5
4	9.6	9.5	9.5	9.6	9.4	2.8
5	7.0	7.5	6.5	7.5	7.0	3.0

For each dive, follow the steps above to calculate the dive's total score.

a. Dive 2 total score: _____   b. Dive 3 total score: _____

c. Dive 4 total score: _____   d. Dive 5 total score: _____

9 How many points altogether were scored on the five dives?

_____

Focus on Problem Solving

Solve the problem, if possible. If a problem has too much information, identify the extra information. If a problem has too little information, describe the information that is needed to solve the problem.

Show your work.

1 Callum lives 346 miles from the beach. He stops for lunch after driving 180 miles. He drives 107 more miles and stops for a snack. How many miles does Callum still have to drive to get to the beach?

_____

2 Mrs. Lin buys 8 packages of pens. Each package contains 12 pens and costs $4. How much does Mrs. Lin spend on pens?

_____

Solve.

3 To support the high school, the local businesses will donate $2 for every ticket sold at the homecoming game. If 113 student, 158 adult, and 52 child tickets were sold, how much money did they donate?

_____

4 Estella, Ringo, and Martin participated in the school walkathon. Estella walked $3\frac{2}{3}$ miles. Ringo walked $\frac{1}{3}$ mile less than Estella, and Martin walked $1\frac{1}{2}$ times as far as Ringo walked. How far did Martin walk?

_____

5 The fifth-grade classes at Keeth Elementary collected a total of 462 cans of food for a food drive. Mr. Becker's class collected 120 cans. The other 3 classes collected the rest of the cans, and each of these three classes collected the same number. How many cans did each of the other classes collect?

_____

Name _____ **Date** _____

PATH to FLUENCY

Multiply.

1
$$\begin{array}{r} 33 \\ \times\ 2 \\ \hline \end{array}$$

2
$$\begin{array}{r} 329 \\ \times\ 8 \\ \hline \end{array}$$

3
$$\begin{array}{r} 608 \\ \times\ 5 \\ \hline \end{array}$$

4
$$\begin{array}{r} 800 \\ \times\ 9 \\ \hline \end{array}$$

5
$$\begin{array}{r} 6{,}295 \\ \times\ 7 \\ \hline \end{array}$$

6
$$\begin{array}{r} 5{,}803 \\ \times\ 6 \\ \hline \end{array}$$

7
$$\begin{array}{r} 7{,}003 \\ \times\ 8 \\ \hline \end{array}$$

8
$$\begin{array}{r} 4{,}000 \\ \times\ 9 \\ \hline \end{array}$$

9
$$\begin{array}{r} 20 \\ \times 80 \\ \hline \end{array}$$

10
$$\begin{array}{r} 92 \\ \times 30 \\ \hline \end{array}$$

11
$$\begin{array}{r} 88 \\ \times 57 \\ \hline \end{array}$$

12
$$\begin{array}{r} 29 \\ \times 19 \\ \hline \end{array}$$

13
$$\begin{array}{r} 37 \\ \times 25 \\ \hline \end{array}$$

14
$$\begin{array}{r} 64 \\ \times 49 \\ \hline \end{array}$$

15
$$\begin{array}{r} 83 \\ \times 56 \\ \hline \end{array}$$

1 The model represents the length of a whale (*w*) and the length of a porpoise (*p*). For numbers 1a–1d, select True or False for the statement.

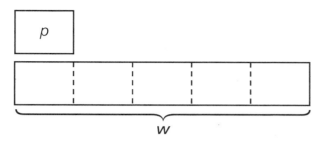

1a. The whale is 5 times as long as the porpoise.   ○ True   ○ False

1b. The porpoise is 5 times as long as the whale.   ○ True   ○ False

1c. The whale is $\frac{1}{5}$ as long as the porpoise.   ○ True   ○ False

1d. The porpoise is $\frac{1}{5}$ as long as the whale.   ○ True   ○ False

Write a word problem for the equation.

2 $\frac{1}{2} \cdot 3 = n$

3 $\frac{5}{8} \cdot n = \frac{10}{8}$

4 $n \div 3 = \frac{1}{6}$

5 Write a word problem for $5 \div \frac{1}{8} = t$.

6 Two students each bought 2 pencils and an eraser. Three students each bought a pen and 3 pencils.

Supply	Cost
pencil	$0.15
eraser	$0.59
pen	$0.49

Select the equation that can be used to find the total cost (c) of the supplies. Mark all that apply.

(A) $c = 2 \times 0.15 + 0.59 + 0.49 + 3 \times 0.15$

(B) $c = 2 \times (2 \times 0.15 + 0.59) + 3 \times (0.49 + 3 \times 0.15)$

(C) $c = 13 \times 0.15 + 2 \times 0.59 + 3 \times 0.49$

(D) $c = 2 \times (0.15 + 0.59) + 3 \times (0.49 + 0.15)$

7 Students in the high school marching band are arranged in 17 equal rows. There are 85 students in the marching band.

Part A

How many students are in each row? Write an equation and use it to solve the problem.

Part B

Explain how you know your answer is reasonable.

8 Penn volunteered a total of 72 hours over the last 12 weeks. He volunteered the same number of hours each week. How many hours did Penn volunteer in one week? Write an equation and use it to solve the problem.

9 Henry has $2\frac{3}{4}$ cups of flour. He uses $1\frac{1}{2}$ cups of the flour to bake muffins. How much flour (*f*) does Henry have left?

Part A

Complete the model to represent this problem.

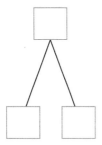

Part B

Write an equation to find out how much flour Henry has left. Then solve.

Without solving the problem, choose the words that make the sentence true.

10 Fido eats 2 cups of kibble. Fifi eats $\frac{6}{5}$ of what Fido eats.

Fifi eats
| more than |
| less than |
| the same as |
Fido.

11 Camille collects stickers. Her sticker book holds 5 stickers in each row. When a page is full, it holds 65 stickers. How many rows (*r*) of stickers are on a full page?

Part A

Complete the area model to represent this problem.

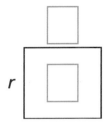

Part B

Write an equation. Then solve.

12 Julianne and Derek made signs for their school spirit week. Julianne made a sign that is $3\frac{1}{2}$ feet long. Derek made a sign that is $\frac{5}{6}$ as long as Julianne's sign. How long is the sign Derek made? Complete the equation.

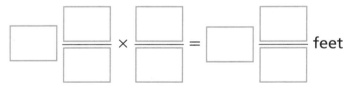

13 Emilio made 65 potholders. Each potholder cost him $1.65 to make. If he sells each potholder for $2.12, how much profit will he make?

$_____

14 Without multiplying the numbers, classify the expression as *less than 3.75* or *greater than 3.75*. Write the letter of the expression in the appropriate box.

A $3\frac{3}{4} \times \frac{9}{10}$ B 1.2×3.75 C $2 \times 3\frac{3}{4}$ D $3\frac{3}{4} \times \frac{1}{2}$ E 3.75×0.75

Less than 3.75	Greater than 3.75

15 Juan and Joe drove 3,200 miles during their vacation. Juan (y) drove 3 times as many miles as Joe (x).

Part A

Draw a model to represent the problem.

Part B

How many miles did each person drive?

16 At an electronics store, a refrigerator costs 3 times as much as a DVD player. A dishwasher costs $125 more than a DVD player.

Part A

Use the numbers to complete the sign.

0	2
4	5
6	7

Item	Price
DVD player	$150
Refrigerator	$ ☐☐☐
Dishwasher	$ ☐☐☐

Part B

Mrs. Shin bought 12 refrigerators and 12 dishwashers for her apartment building. She received a discount of $90 on the entire purchase. Write an equation using parentheses to find the amount she owes. Then solve.

17 For numbers 17a–17e, choose Yes or No to indicate whether the comparison is additive.

17a. 250 times as long   ○ Yes   ○ No

17b. 123 more than   ○ Yes   ○ No

17c. $2.56 less than   ○ Yes   ○ No

17d. in $\frac{1}{2}$ the time   ○ Yes   ○ No

17e. 3.2 fewer seconds   ○ Yes   ○ No

18 Jerome scores 12 points in a basketball game. This is twice the number of points that Jaime scores. How many points did the rest of the team score? Solve the problem if possible. Identify extra information or information that is needed to solve the problem.

19 A car is 234 inches long. A model of the car is $\frac{1}{18}$ times the size of the actual car. Without solving the problem, select the answer that is the most reasonable length of the model of the car.

(A) $\frac{13}{18}$ inches

(B) 13 inches

(C) 216 inches

(D) 4,212 inches

20 A python (*p*) is 1.5 feet longer than a boa constrictor (*b*). Choose an expression from each column to create an equation that compares the lengths of the snakes.

○ b + 1.5		○ p − 1.5
○ 1.5b	=	○ 1.5p
○ b		○ p + 1.5
○ b − 1.5		○ p

Making Berry Equations

Carla buys 4 pounds of blueberries at a farmers market. She buys $\frac{3}{4}$ as many pounds of raspberries as blueberries, and $1\frac{1}{2}$ times as many pounds of strawberries as blueberries.

1 Without solving, predict whether Carla buys more raspberries or strawberries. Justify your answer.

_____

_____

_____

_____

_____

2 Find the number of pounds of raspberries and the number of pounds of strawberries that Carla buys. Write a word sentence that uses addition or multiplication to compare the two amounts.

_____

_____

3 What is one way to write and solve an equation to find the total amount of berries Carla buys? Show your work.

_____

_____

4 What is one method you can use to check that your solution is reasonable? Explain why the method works.

_____

_____

_____

_____

Carla returns to the farmers market to buy several different fruits and vegetables.

Fruit and Vegetable Prices	
Item	**Price**
Cherries	$3.80 per pound
Bananas	$0.60 per pound
Coconuts	$4 each
Squash	$2.50 per pound
Broccoli	$3 per head

5 Use the chart to write a multistep problem about the total cost of the items Carla buys. Then write and solve an equation to solve the problem.

_____

_____

_____

6 Carla buys some coconuts and bananas to make pies for a total of $10.40. If she buys 2 coconuts, how many pounds of bananas does she buy? Explain how you solved the problem.

_____

_____

7 The cost per pound for tomatoes is $0.30 more than twice the cost per pound for bananas. Write and solve an equation to find the cost of 4 pounds of tomatoes.

_____

_____

8 Carla still needs to buy some broccoli, squash, and cherries. She has only $15.00 left. Give a combination of how much she can buy of each if she spends more than $10.00. Then determine how much money she will have left after making the purchase. Show your work.

_____

_____

Dear Family:

In our math class, we are studying algebra and operations. Your child will explore simplifying expressions using the Order of Operations.

Your child will generate ordered pairs from verbal rules and equations and use the first quadrant of the coordinate plane to graph the x- and y-coordinates. An example, $y = 2x$, is shown below.

x	1	2	3	4
y	2	4	6	8

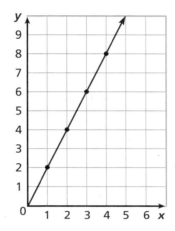

Negative numbers are introduced to your child for the first time in this unit using real world situations involving temperatures, electric charges, and bank balances. The concept that the opposite of a number is the number that is the same distance from zero but in the opposite direction will be explored using number lines.

Your child will extend his or her graphing skills by interpreting and making double bar graphs and line graphs. He or she will make a survey to test a hypothesis and then graph the data. The statistical measures of mean, median, and range will be presented to provide an informal introduction to work with data and statistics.

You can be an active part of your child's learning by asking your child to provide answers or examples for the following questions:

- What algebraic expression describes "4 more than the product of 2 and c"? ($4 + 2 \cdot c$)
- Generate the first five terms of a pattern with the rule *Add 5*. (Possible answer: 0, 5, 10, 15, 20)
- For the ordered pair (4, 6), which is the x-coordinate and which is the y-coordinate? (The x-coordinate is 4 and the y-coordinate is 6.)
- What is the opposite of –4° F? (4° F or +4° F)

Sincerely,
Your child's teacher

Estimada familia:

En nuestra clase de matemáticas, estamos estudiando álgebra y operaciones. Su niño aprenderá cómo simplificar expresiones usando el Orden de las operaciones.

Su niño generará pares ordenados de reglas verbales y ecuaciones y usará el primer cuadrante del plano de coordenadas para hacer una gráfica de la coordenada x y de la coordenada y. El ejemplo, $y = 2x$, se muestra abajo.

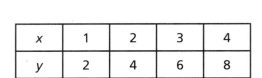

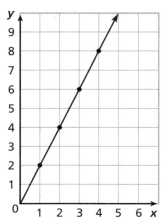

Se presentarán los números negativos a su niño por primera vez en esta unidad usando situaciones de la vida real que implican temperaturas, cargas eléctricas y balances bancarios. El concepto de que lo opuesto de un número es el número que está a la misma distancia de cero, pero en la dirección opuesta se explorará utilizando rectas numéricas.

Su niño ampliará sus habilidades gráficas interpretando y haciendo gráficas de doble barra y gráficas lineales. Hará una encuesta para probar una hipótesis y luego graficar los datos. Las medidas estadísticas de la media, la mediana y el rango se presentarán para proporcionar una introducción informal para trabajar con datos y estadísticas.

Usted puede participar activamente en el aprendizaje de su niño, pidiéndole que responda las siguientes preguntas:

- ¿Qué expresión algebraica describe "4 más que el producto de 2 por c"? $(4 + 2 \cdot c)$

- Genera los primeros cinco términos de un patrón, usando la regla *"Suma 5"*. (Respuesta posible: 0, 5, 10, 15, 20)

- Para el par ordenado (4, 6), ¿cuál es la coordenada x y cuál es la coordenada y? (La coordenada x es 4 y la coordenada y es 6.)

- ¿Qué es lo opuesto de –4° F? (4° F o +4° F)

Atentamente,
El maestro de su niño

Read and Write Expressions

coordinate plane

expression

double bar graph

function

evaluate

hypothesis

A number, variable, or a combination of numbers and variables with one or more operations.

Examples:

4

t

$6 \cdot n$

$4 \div p + 5$

$5 \times 4 + 3 \times 7$

$6 \cdot (x + 2)$

A system of coordinates formed by the perpendicular intersection of horizontal and vertical number lines.

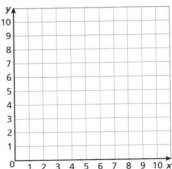

A relationship between two sets of numbers. Each number in one set is paired with exactly one number in the other set. A function can be described by an equation, a table of ordered pairs of numbers (an input/output table), a verbal rule, or a graph.

A graph that uses vertical or horizontal bars to compare data for two groups.

Example:

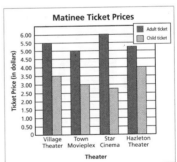

A statement used as a basis of an investigation.

Example:
Survey: Students' favorite breakfast foods Possible hypothesis: Most students will choose pancakes as their favorite breakfast.

To substitute values for the variables in an expression and then simplify the resulting expression.

Examples:
Evaluate $7 + 5 \cdot n$ for $n = 2$.

$7 + 5 \cdot n = 7 + 5 \cdot 2$ **Substitute 2 for n.**

$= 7 + 10$ **Multiply.**

$= 17$ **Add.**

inequality	mean
integers	median
line graph	negative numbers

© Houghton Mifflin Harcourt Publishing Company

The sum of the values in a set of data divided by the number of values.

A mathematical sentence that contains > (is greater than), < (is less than), ≥ (is greater than or equal to), ≤ (is less than or equal to), or ≠ (is not equal to).

Examples:

$a > 5$

$14 \leq b + 3$

The middle value when the values in a set of data are listed in order from least to greatest or greatest to least. When there are two middle values, the median is the mean of the two middle values.

All whole numbers
(0, 1, 2, 3, …) and their opposites
… $^-3$, $^-2$, 1, 0, $^+1$, $^+2$, $^+3$…

The numbers to the left of, or below, zero on a number line.

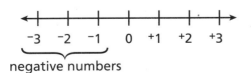

negative numbers

A graph that uses a line or line segments to show how a quantity changes over time.

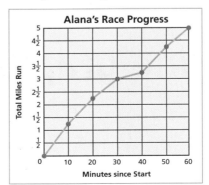

numerical pattern

ordered pair

opposites

origin

Order of Operations

positive numbers

A pair of numbers that shows the position of a point on a coordinate plane.

Example:

The ordered pair (3, 4) represents a point 3 units to the right of the *y*-axis and 4 units above the *x*-axis.

A sequence of numbers that share a relationship.

Example:

In this numerical pattern, each term is 3 more than the term before.

2, 5, 8, 11, 14, . . .

The point (0, 0) on the coordinate plane.

Two numbers that are the same distance from zero on a number line but in opposite directions.

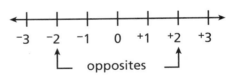

The numbers to the right of, or above, zero on a number line.

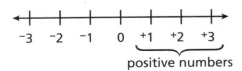

A rule that states the order in which the operations in an expression should be done:

Step 1: Perform operations inside parentheses.

Step 2: Multiply and divide from left to right.

Step 3: Add and subtract from left to right.

range

variable

simplify an expression

x-axis

term

x-coordinate

A letter or other symbol used to stand for an unknown number in an algebraic expression.

The difference between the least (or minimum) value in a set of data and the greatest (or maximum) value.

The horizontal axis of the coordinate plane.

Use the Order of Operations to find the value of the expression.

Example:
Simplify 6 • (2 + 5) ÷ 3.

6 • (2 + 5) ÷ 3 = 6 • 7 ÷ 3
$$= 42 ÷ 3$$
$$= 14$$

The first number in an ordered pair, which represents a point's horizontal distance from the *y*-axis.

Example:
The *x-coordinate* of the point represented by the ordered pair (3, 4) is 3.

Each number in a numerical pattern.

Example:
In the pattern below, 3 is the first term, and 9 is the fourth term.

3, 5, 7, 9, 11, . . .

y-axis

y-coordinate

The vertical axis of the
coordinate plane.

The second number in an
ordered pair, which represents a
point's vertical distance from the
x-axis.

Example:
The *y*-coordinate of the point represented by
the ordered pair (3, 4) is 4.

Simple Expressions

VOCABULARY
expression

Below are some **expressions**. An expression does not have an equal sign.

$\frac{1}{2} + \frac{2}{3}$ $24 \div 3$ $5 \cdot (6 - 2)$ $6 + n$ $12 - 10 \times 0.4$

Expressions use numbers and symbols to "express" computations.

Expression	Computation in Words
$3.5 + 6.3$	Add 3.5 and 6.3.
$10 - 2$	Subtract 2 from 10.
$\frac{1}{2} \cdot p$	Multiply p by $\frac{1}{2}$.
$14 \div 4$	Divide 14 by 4.

There is more than one way to say some of the computations above. For example, for $3.5 + 6.3$, you also could say, "Find the sum of 3.5 and 6.3."

1 What is another way to say $\frac{1}{2} \cdot p$?

_____

Write the computation in words.

2 $7.5 - 2.25$ _____

3 $b + 9$ _____

4 $\frac{3}{4} \cdot 8 \cdot \frac{1}{2}$ _____

5 $1.6 \div 0.2$ _____

Write an expression for the words.

6 Find the product of 12 and 0.1. _____

7 Subtract $\frac{2}{3}$ from $3\frac{1}{2}$. _____

8 Add 14 and t. _____

9 Divide p by q. _____

Expressions with More than One Operation

VOCABULARY
Order of Operations

When you read and write expressions with more than one operation, think about the **Order of Operations**.

$11 \cdot 15 + 3$ Multiply 11 and 15 and then add 3.

$11 \cdot (15 + 3)$ Add 15 and 3 and then multiply by 11.

Order of Operations

Step 1 Perform operations inside parentheses.

Step 2 Multiply and divide from left to right.

Step 3 Add and subtract from left to right.

⑩ Consider the expression $12 \div (5 + 2)$.

a. Which operation is done first, division or addition?

_____

b. Write the computation in words.

_____

⑪ Consider the expression $12 \div 5 + 2$.

a. Which operation is done first? _____

b. Write the computation in words.

_____

Write the computation in words. Think about the Order of Operations.

⑫ $3.5 - (2.1 + 1.2)$ _____

⑬ $\frac{1}{2} + \frac{3}{4} \cdot t$ _____

⑭ $(25 - 10) \div 5$ _____

Write an expression for the words. Think about the Order of Operations.

⑮ Multiply the sum of p and 3 by 0.1. _____

⑯ Divide 36 by 4 and then add 3. _____

⑰ Add the product of 2 and 5 to the product of 9 and 8.

_____

✓ **Check Understanding**

Discuss why the two expressions $8 + 7 \cdot 4$ and $(8 + 7) \cdot 4$ have different values.

Read and Write Expressions

Simplify Expressions

VOCABULARY
simplify an expression

If an expression does not have a letter, or variable, then you can **simplify** it to find its value. For example, you can simplify $15 \div 3$ to get 5.

How do you simplify an expression that has more than one operation? For example, when you simplify $12 - 3 \cdot 2$, do you subtract first or multiply first?

The Order of Operations tells us that to simplify $12 - 3 \cdot 2$, we multiply first and then subtract.

Order of Operations

Step 1 Perform operations inside parentheses.

Step 2 Multiply and divide from left to right.

Step 3 Add and subtract from left to right.

$$12 - 3 \cdot 2 = 12 - 6 \qquad \text{Multiply.}$$
$$= 6 \qquad \text{Subtract.}$$

1 Follow the Order of Operations to simplify $25 - (5 + 2) \cdot 3$.

Step 1 Perform operations inside parentheses.   _____

Step 2 Multiply and divide from left to right.   _____

Step 3 Add and subtract from left to right.   _____

Simplify. Follow the Order of Operations.

2 $5 + 16 \div 4$

3 $10 \cdot (0.3 + 0.2)$

4 $20 \div 4 + 3 \cdot 3$

5 $\left(\frac{5}{6} - \frac{1}{3}\right) \cdot 4$

6 $21 - 12 + 9 - 2$

7 $6 \times (2 + 4) \div 3$

8 $0.3 + 0.1 \cdot 5 + 0.2$

9 $18 + 9 \div 0.1$

10 $36 \div (3 \cdot 2)$

Grouping Symbols

Parentheses group parts of an expression together and let you know which operations to do first. Brackets, [ ], and braces, { }, are also grouping symbols. These symbols are often used when an expression has grouping symbols inside other grouping symbols.

To simplify an expression with grouping symbols inside other grouping symbols, work from the inside out.

$$12 \cdot [48 \div (4 + 4)] = 12 \cdot [48 \div 8] \quad \text{Add inside the parentheses.}$$
$$= 12 \cdot 6 \quad \text{Divide inside the brackets.}$$
$$= 72 \quad \text{Multiply.}$$

Simplify.

11 $6 \cdot (12 - 4) \div 16$ **12** $(1.3 + 2.7) \div (2.2 - 1.7)$ **13** $10 - \{8 \div [4 \div (2 \div 1)]\}$

What's the Error?

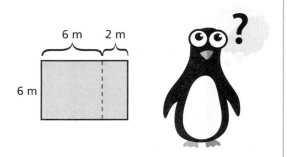

Dear Math Students,

I wrote the expression $6 \cdot 6 + 2$ for the area of the rectangle at the right. My friend said, "You forgot the parentheses." Can you explain what my friend meant?

Your friend,
Puzzled Penguin

6 m   2 m

6 m

14 Write a response to Puzzled Penguin.

_____

_____

_____

✓ Check Understanding

Explain how to simplify $100 \div [(12 - 7) \cdot 2]$. Show your steps.

Simplify Expressions

Expressions with Variables

VOCABULARY
evaluate
variable

The expressions below contain letters, or **variables**.
A variable represents an unknown number.

$3\frac{1}{2} + x$ $n \div 0.01$ $5 \cdot (p - 2)$ $t - 6$ $4 + 10 \times w$

To **evaluate** an expression, substitute a value for
the variable and then use the Order of Operations
to simplify.

Evaluate $5 \cdot (p - 2)$ for $p = 10$.

$5 \cdot (p - 2) = 5 \cdot (10 - 2)$ Substitute 10 for p.
$ = 5 \cdot 8$ Subtract inside parentheses.
$ = 40$ Multiply.

Order of Operations

Step 1 Perform operations inside parentheses.

Step 2 Multiply and divide from left to right.

Step 3 Add and subtract from left to right.

Evaluate the expression.

1 $m - 4.7$ for $m = 10$

2 $5 \div x$ for $x = \frac{1}{3}$

3 $5 + n \cdot 4$ for $n = 3$

4 $\frac{1}{5} \cdot x$ for $x = 15$

5 $7.5 \times (d - 2.5)$ for $d = 3.5$

6 $48 \div (z - 6)$ for $z = 14$

7 $10 \cdot (0.05 + q)$ for $q = 1.2$

8 $2\frac{3}{4} + d - 1\frac{1}{4} + 5\frac{1}{2}$ for $d = 1\frac{1}{2}$

9 $1,000 \cdot h$ for $h = 0.004$

10 $(t + 18) \div 5$ for $t = 17$

11 $54 \div 3 \cdot v$ for $v = 3$

12 $6 \cdot 0.01 + n \cdot 0.1$ for $n = 2$

Real World Expressions

13 Four friends earned $24 by washing cars and m dollars by mowing lawns. They want to divide the total equally.

a. Write an expression for the amount each friend gets.

_____

b. If they made $50 mowing lawns, how much should each friend get?

_____

14 There are $\frac{2}{3}$ as many students in science club as in math club.

a. If there are m students in math club, how many are in science club?

_____

b. If there are 27 students in math club, how many are in science club?

_____

15 Kima's cat weighs 6 pounds more than her rabbit. Her dog weighs 3 times as much as her cat. Let r be the weight of Kima's rabbit.

a. How much does her cat weigh?

_____

b. How much does her dog weigh?

_____

c. If Kima's rabbit weighs 5 pounds, how much do her cat and dog weigh?

_____

16 To change a temperature from degrees Celsius to degrees Fahrenheit, multiply it by $\frac{9}{5}$ and then add 32.

a. Let c be a temperature in degrees Celsius. Write an expression for changing c to degrees Fahrenheit.

_____

b. Use your expression to change 20°C to degrees Fahrenheit.

_____

Expressions, Equations, and Inequalities

Name _____

Substitute Values in an Equation

For each equation, substitute the given value for the variable. Write *true* or *false* for the equation that results.

⑰ $20 \cdot (x - 5) = 100$

    a. $x = 15$ _____

    b. $x = 10$ _____

    c. $x = 7$ _____

⑱ $(16 + b) \div 2 = 11$

    a. $b = 10$ _____

    b. $b = 3$ _____

    c. $b = 6$ _____

⑲ $0.68 = 3.4 \cdot k$

    a. $k = 2$ _____

    b. $k = 0.2$ _____

    c. $k = 0.02$ _____

Equation Situations

Choose the equation that represents each situation.

⑳ Greg starts a computer club with 9 of his friends. He hopes to get 5 more people to join each month. Which equation shows the number of months (m) it will take to have 45 people in the computer club?

    a. $45 - 9 = 5 \cdot m$ b. $10 + 5 \cdot m = 45$ c. $(10 + 5) \cdot m = 45$

㉑ Furry Friends Pet Rescue Shelter has 32 animals that need homes. If 4 animals are adopted each week but 5 new animals arrive each week, which equation shows the number of weeks (w) that will have passed when there are 40 animals at the shelter?

    a. $32 - (5 + 4) \cdot w = 40$ b. $32 + (5 - 4) \cdot w = 40$ c. $40 = 32 + 5 + w$

㉒ Write a real world situation to represent the equation $35 - n = 16$.

_____

_____

㉓ Write a real world situation to represent the equation $50 \div n = 10$.

_____

_____

Inequalities with Variables

VOCABULARY
inequality

You can find variables in an inequality also, such as $d > 5$, $d < 10$, or $d \neq 5$.

For each inequality, substitute the given value for the variable. Write *true* or *false* for the inequality that results.

24 $12 - g > 4.5$

a. $g = 6.5$ _____   b. $g = 7.5$ _____   c. $g = 8.5$ _____

25 $60 \leq d - 13$

a. $d = 47$ _____   b. $d = 50$ _____   c. $d = 73$ _____

Inequality Situations

Choose the inequality that represents each situation.

26 Julie's exercise goal is to walk more than 10 miles each week. Which inequality shows the number of miles (m) she wants to walk next week?

a. $m > 10$ b. $m < 10$ c. $m \leq 10$

27 Mr. Okano announced that no more than 250 students can go on the spring field trip. Which inequality shows the number of students (s) who can go on the trip?

a. $s \geq 250$ b. $s \neq 250$ c. $s \leq 250$

28 Write a real world situation to represent the inequality $k < 150$.

_____

_____

29 Write a real world situation to represent the inequality $f \geq 4\frac{1}{2}$.

_____

_____

Check Understanding

Explain how an expression, an equation, and an inequality are different.

Expressions, Equations, and Inequalities

Write the correct answer.

1 Write 3.5 · 4 using words.

_____

Use the Order of Operations to simplify the expression.

2 $30 - 7 \cdot 4$

_____

3 $5 + (21 - 6) \div 0.2$

_____

4 Evaluate the expression.

$\frac{2}{3} \cdot 6 + \frac{2}{3} \cdot n$ for $n = 2$

_____

5 Write a real world situation to represent the equation $34 \div n = 17$.

_____

_____

_____

Name _____ **Date** _____

Multiply.

1 30
  × 4

2 25
  × 7

3 500
  × 3

4 320
  × 8

5 507
  × 6

6 814
  × 5

7 128
  × 9

8 7,000
  × 9

9 4,060
  × 3

10 5,809
  × 6

11 3,793
  × 4

12 20
  ×30

13 45
  ×60

14 63
  ×79

15 36
  ×89

Patterns and Expressions

VOCABULARY
numerical pattern
term

A **numerical pattern** is a sequence of numbers that share a relationship. Each number in a numerical pattern is a **term**. Below we show the first five terms of a pattern.

$$3, 5, 7, 9, 11, \ldots$$

The pattern above starts with 3, and then each term is two more than the previous term. You can write numerical expressions for the terms. We show two possible expressions for each term below.

3	5	7	9	11
↑	↑	↑	↑	↑

Expressions
$$3 \qquad 3 + 2 \qquad 3 + 2 + 2 \qquad 3 + 2 + 2 + 2 \qquad 3 + 2 + 2 + 2 + 2$$
$$3 \qquad 3 + (1 \cdot 2) \qquad 3 + (2 \cdot 2) \qquad 3 + (3 \cdot 2) \qquad 3 + (4 \cdot 2)$$

Solve.

1 a. Write two expressions for the next term (the sixth term) in the pattern 3, 5, 7, 9, 11 . . .

_____

   b. Write the sixth term. _____

2 a. Write the first five terms of a numerical pattern that begins with 5 and then adds 5.

_____

   b. Write an expression for the sixth term of the pattern.

_____

   c. Write the sixth term. _____

3 a. Write the first five terms of a numerical pattern that begins with 1 and then adds 9.

_____

   b. Write an expression for the sixth term of the pattern.

_____

   c. Write the sixth term. _____

Patterns and Relationships

Solve.

4 a. Write the first five terms of a pattern that begins with 2, and then adds 2.

___ ___ ___ ___ ___

b. Write the first five terms of a pattern that begins with 4, and then adds 4.

___ ___ ___ ___ ___

c. Circle the corresponding pairs of terms in the patterns. How does each term in the top pattern compare with the corresponding term in the bottom pattern?

_____

d. How does the bottom term compare with the top term?

_____

5 a. Write the first five terms of a pattern that begins with 9, and then adds 9.

___ ___ ___ ___ ___

b. Write the first five terms of a pattern that begins with 3, and then adds 3.

___ ___ ___ ___ ___

c. Circle the corresponding pairs of terms in the patterns. How does each term in the top pattern compare with the corresponding term in the bottom pattern?

_____

d. How does the bottom term compare with the top term?

_____

6 a. Write the first five terms of two different patterns.

___ ___ ___ ___ ___

___ ___ ___ ___ ___

b. If possible, describe two different relationships that the corresponding terms of your patterns share.

_____

_____

Patterns and Relationships

Name _____

Real World Patterns

Many situations in your everyday life can be described by numerical patterns. The table below shows late fees for an overdue library book. Complete the table.

Overdue Book Late Fee					
Number of Days Late	1	2	3	4	5
Late Fee	15¢	30¢			

7 Describe the relationship between the corresponding terms.

_____

_____

Complete the table and describe the relationship between corresponding terms.

8

Bicycles and Wheels					
Bicycles	0	1	3	4	7
Wheels	0	2			

_____

_____

9

Cost of Concert Tickets					
Tickets	1	2	3	4	5
Cost in Dollars		70	105		

_____

_____

10

Weather Relationships					
Inches of Rain	0	0.5	1	1.5	2
Inches of Snow	0	5	10		

_____

_____

What's the Error?

Dear Math Students,

I was asked to predict the sixth term of the following pattern.

$$1, 2, 4, 8, 16, \dots$$

I know that I can predict any term of a pattern if I first identify the rule of the pattern.

I compared the first and second terms and decided that the second term is produced by adding 1.

I compared the second and third terms and decided that the third term is produced by adding 2.

1	2	4	8	16	21?
↓	↓	↓			↑
1	1 + 1	2 + 2	4 + 3	8 + 4	16 + 5

I began to recognize a pattern, which was add 1 to find the second term, add 2 to find the third term, and so on. So I decided to add 5 to find the sixth term, and I wrote 16 + 5, or 21, for my answer.

The correct answer is 32. Can you help me understand what I did wrong?

Your Friend,

Puzzled Penguin

11 Write a response to Puzzled Penguin.

_____

_____

_____

_____

_____

✓ Check Understanding

Look at the two patterns of numbers. Identify the corresponding terms of those patterns, and describe a relationship that the terms share.

1, 3, 5, 7, 9, …
3, 9, 15, 21, 27, …

Patterns and Relationships

Name _____

Read Points

VOCABULARY
coordinate plane
ordered pair
origin
x-axis
x-coordinate
y-axis
y-coordinate

A **coordinate plane** is formed by the intersection of a horizontal number line, called the **x-axis**, and a vertical number line, called the **y-axis**.

Use the coordinate plane below to answer the questions.

1 An **ordered pair** is used to describe the location of any point in the coordinate plane. For example, the ordered pair (9, 5) describes the location of point *A*. An ordered pair consists of an **x-coordinate** and a **y-coordinate**.

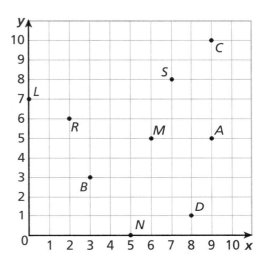

a. The first coordinate, the *x*-coordinate, represents distance along which axis?

_____

b. The second coordinate, the *y*-coordinate, represents distance along which axis?

_____

2 The **origin** of the coordinate plane is the point at (0, 0). Why is the origin an important point?

_____

_____

Write an ordered pair to represent the location of each point.

3 point *B* _____   4 point *C* _____   5 point *D* _____   6 point *L* _____

7 point *M* _____   8 point *N* _____   9 point *R* _____   10 point *S* _____

Plot Points

Use the coordinate plane below to complete Exercises 11–25.

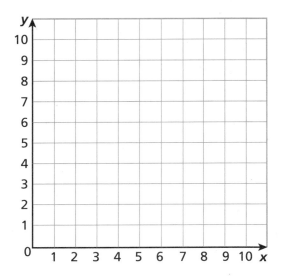

Plot and label a point at each location.

11 point *J* at (5, 4)   **12** point *Q* at (1, 9)   **13** point *Y* at (2, 0)

14 point *W* at (0, 4)   **15** point *K* at (4, 5)   **16** point *R* at (8, 3)

17 point *B* at (6, 1)   **18** point *V* at (3, 8)   **19** point *L* at (10, 0)

20 point *P* at (7, 10)   **21** point *C* at (0, 6)   **22** point *Z* at (9, 7)

On the coordinate plane above, draw an angle of the given type. The angle should have its vertex at one labeled point and sides that pass through two other labeled points. Give the name of the angle.

23 acute angle _____

24 obtuse angle _____

25 right angle _____

The Coordinate Plane

Name _____

Horizontal and Vertical Distance

26 Plot a point at (1, 10). Label the point *A*.
Plot a point at (1, 7). Label the point *B*.
Plot a point at (8, 10). Label the point *C*.
Plot a point at (8, 7). Label the point *D*.
Connect the points to form a quadrilateral.

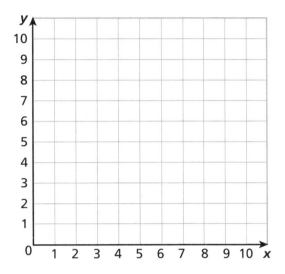

27 Explain how subtraction can be used to find the lengths of line segments *AB* and *AC*.

_____

_____

_____

_____

28 In the coordinate plane above, draw a rectangle that is not a square.

29 What ordered pairs represent the vertices of the rectangle?

_____

30 Write a subtraction equation to represent the length of the rectangle, and write a subtraction equation to represent its width.

_____

What's the Error?

Dear Math Students,

I was asked to name the location of a fourth point that would form a square when the points are connected by line segments.

I think the point (7, 4) would form a square.

Do you think that is correct?

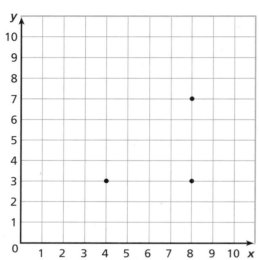

Your friend,
Puzzled Penguin

31 Write a response to Puzzled Penguin.

_____

_____

_____

_____

_____

✓ Check Understanding

Explain how to locate a point with the coordinates (5, 2) on a coordinate plane. Explain how you know that point is not on the x- or y-axis just by looking at the coordinates.

Generate and Graph Ordered Pairs

Numerical patterns can be written horizontally or vertically. The *add 4* table below shows a numerical pattern in the left column and the result of adding 4 in the right column.

add 4	
1	5
2	
3	
4	
5	

(x, y)
(1, 5)
(___, ___)
(___, ___)
(___, ___)
(___, ___)

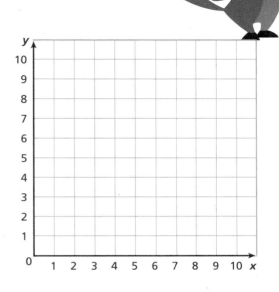

1 Complete the *add 4* table.

2 Complete the (x, y) table to show the ordered pairs that the *add 4* table represents.

3 Each ordered pair represents a point in the coordinate plane. Graph and connect the points.

Suppose a shrub grows at the rate shown in the table below. Use the table to complete Exercises 4 and 5.

Growth of a Shrub	
Age (years)	Height (feet)
0	0
1	1
2	2
3	3
4	4

4 Write five ordered pairs that the data represent.

_____

5 Graph the ordered pairs and connect the points. What does each axis of the graph represent?

_____

_____

Real World Problems

Every 20 minutes, a dripping faucet leaks 10 mL of water.

6 Complete the table to show the amount of water that will leak in 0, 40, and 60 minutes.

Time (min)	0	20	40	60
Amount of Water (mL)		10		

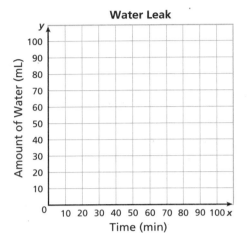

Water Leak

7 Write the ordered pairs (x, y) that the data represent. Then graph and connect the points and extend the line.

(____, ____) (____, ____) (____, ____) (____, ____)

8 What amount of water would you expect to leak in 90 minutes? Explain your answer.

_____

_____

_____

The graph below represents an automobile traveling at a constant speed.

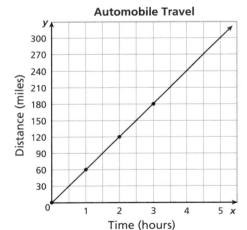

Automobile Travel

9 The points on the graph represent four ordered pairs (x, y). Write the ordered pairs.

(____, ____) (____, ____) (____, ____) (____, ____)

10 Complete the table to show the relationship between time and distance.

Time (hours)	0			
Distance (miles)	0			

11 At what constant rate of speed was the automobile traveling? Explain how you know.

_____

_____

Graph Ordered Pairs

Name _____

Graph a Function

VOCABULARY
function

A **function** can be described by an equation, by a table that shows ordered pairs of numbers, by a verbal rule, or by a line on a coordinate graph made by connecting ordered pairs.

12 Mindy and her friends are planning to walk for a charity. They will earn the same number of dollars (*d*) for each mile (*m*) they walk. Fill in the four tables to show what they could earn for charity.

$d = m$	
m	*d*
0	0
1	___
2	___
3	___
4	___
5	___

$d = 2m$	
m	*d*
0	___
1	___
2	___
3	___
4	___
5	___

$d = 3m$	
m	*d*
0	___
1	___
2	___
3	___
4	___
5	___

$d = 5m$	
m	*d*
0	___
1	___
2	___
3	___
4	___
5	___

13 For each table, graph the ordered pairs and connect the points with a line (use your ruler to draw the line). Label each line with its equation.

14 Give two coordinate pairs you could use to graph $d = 4m$.

(_____, _____) and (_____, _____)

Draw and label this line.

15 Describe relationships you see between the values of *m* and *d* for each equation.

_____

_____

_____

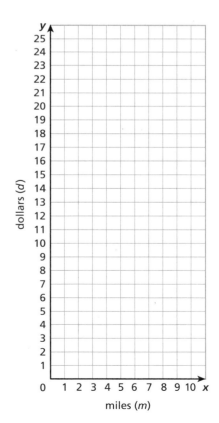

Use a Verbal Rule to Graph a Function

Functions can also describe additive relationships. In these tables, s is the age of a sister and b is the age of a brother. Discuss what each table tells you about their ages.

$s = b$	
b	s
0	___
1	___
2	___
3	___
4	___
5	___

$s = b + 1$	
b	s
0	___
1	___
2	___
3	___
4	___
5	___

$s = b + 2$	
b	s
0	___
1	___
2	___
3	___
4	___
5	___

$s = b + 3$	
b	s
0	___
1	___
2	___
3	___
4	___
5	___

$s = b + 4$	
b	s
0	___
1	___
2	___
3	___
4	___
5	___

16 For each table, graph the ordered pairs and connect the points with a line (use your ruler to draw the line). Label each line with its equation.

17 Give two coordinate pairs you could use to graph $s = b + 10$.

(_____, _____) and (_____, _____)

Draw and label this line.

18 Describe relationships you see.

_____

_____

_____

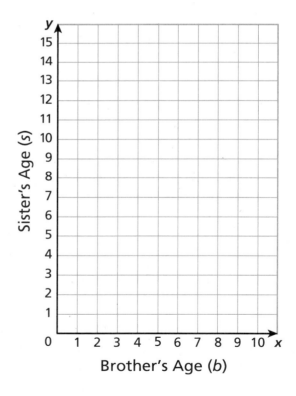

✓ Check Understanding

The graph of $s = b + 2.5$ would be between the graphs of which two rules shown above?

_____

Math and Constellations

An *astronomer* is a scientist who studies objects in space such as stars, planets, and galaxies.

Although you can see only a few thousand stars when you look into the night sky, astronomers have used special instruments to find and catalogue more than 800,000 different stars.

Constellations are patterns of a few bright stars that form pictures in the night sky. The well-known constellation Orion is shown at the right. Some people interpret the arrangement of stars as a hunter with a bow; others as a warrior with a shield.

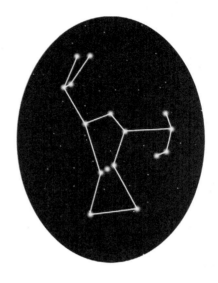

Solve.

1 The grid at the right shows the constellation Gemini. Gemini is sometimes called "The Twins." On the lines below, write the coordinates of the points that form Gemini.

_____

_____

_____

_____

2 The points shown below form another well-known constellation that is sometimes called "The Big Dipper."

(0, 3) (2, 4) (4, 3) (5, 2) (5, 0) (7, 0) (8, 2)

On the grid at the right, plot the points. Then connect the points in the order in which you plotted them to form the Big Dipper.

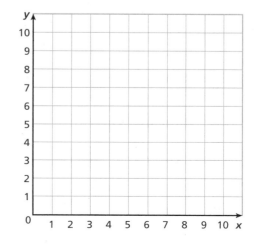

Math and Constellations (continued)

The star Polaris is called the North Star because it appears as if it is located above Earth's North Pole. Polaris is also well known because all the stars in the sky appear to revolve around it.

The picture at the right was taken by pointing a camera at Polaris and leaving the lens open for several hours.

3 To find Polaris in the night sky, first find the Big Dipper. A ray drawn from the two stars shown at the right edge of the Big Dipper always points toward Polaris.

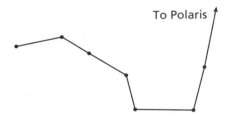

To Polaris

Look back at the Big Dipper you drew for Exercise 2. On the grid, draw a point where Polaris could be located. Write the coordinates of the point you drew.

_____

4 Another well known constellation is the Summer Triangle. Plot and connect the points (5, 1), (2, 10), and (8, 8) to form the Summer Triangle. Name the triangle according to the lengths of its sides.

_____

_____

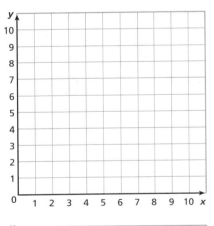

5 The points below form the constellation Bootes, which looks like a kite that has two tails. Plot the points and connect them in the order in which you plotted them.

(7, 5) (4, 6) (2, 7) (2, 9) (5, 9) (6, 7) (7, 5)

Form the tails of the kite by plotting points at (5, 3) and (8, 5). Connect each point to the point at (7, 5).

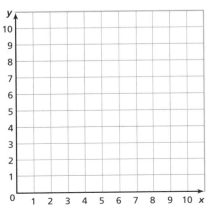

Focus on Problem Solving

Solve.

1 Write the next four terms in each pattern. Then describe a relationship between the corresponding terms in the two patterns.

Add 4	4				
Add 12	12				

_____

_____

2 Write the next two terms in the pattern. Then describe the relationship between the corresponding terms in the two patterns.

Hats	1	2	3	4	5
Sequins	18	36	54		

_____

_____

3 Write the ordered pairs that represent the vertices of the rectangle.

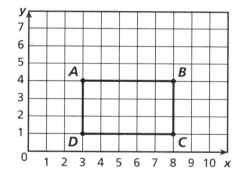

_____

4 Write the ordered pairs that the data represent.

Add 6	
1	7
2	8
3	9
4	10

_____

5 Write three other ordered pairs for the equation $y = 2x$. Then graph the ordered pairs on the coordinate grid.

(1, 2), _____

_____

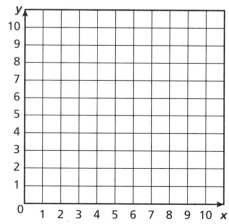

Name _____   Date _____

Multiply.

1 40
    × 5

2 26
    × 8

3 600
    × 4

4 809
    × 7

5 380
    × 6

6 712
    × 9

7 784
    × 3

8 8,000
    × 6

9 5,100
    × 7

10 3,980
     × 5

11 5,297
     × 8

12 40
     × 10

13 32
     × 30

14 31
     × 78

15 63
     × 89

Name _____

Discuss Real World Situations

Discuss each situation and diagram.

1 Whales often dive from the surface of the ocean to great depths. Orcas or killer whales are known to dive as deep as 250 meters below sea level.

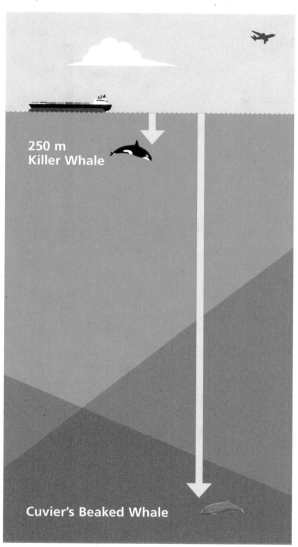

250 m
Killer Whale

Cuvier's Beaked Whale

A Cuvier's beaked whale may dive 12 times as deep as a killer whale. How would you describe how deep the beaked whale dives?

_____

_____

2 A checking account has a balance of $278.

Check Number	Amount	Balance
		$278.00

Suppose a check is written for $300.

Check Number	Amount	Balance
		$278.00
206	$300.00	−$300.00

Using words, describe the new balance.

_____

_____

3 A helium atom is made up of 2 protons, 2 neutrons, and 2 electrons. A proton has an electrical charge of ⁺1, a neutron has no charge (0), and an electron has an electrical charge of ⁻1.

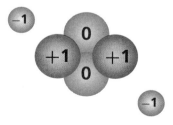

Is there a positive electrical charge for every negative electrical charge in the helium atom?

_____

_____

Identify and Write Opposite Temperatures

VOCABULARY
opposites

Two numbers are **opposites** if they are the same distance from zero on a number line but in opposite directions. If two temperatures are opposites, they are the same distance from zero on a thermometer. If one temperature is above zero, its opposite will be below zero. The opposite of zero is zero.

Each arrow on the Fahrenheit thermometer points to a temperature. Write the temperature.

4 _____

5 _____

6 _____

7 _____

8 _____

9 _____

10 _____

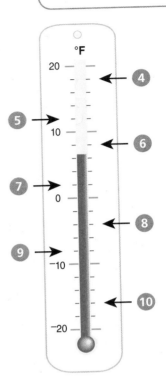

Each arrow on the Celsius thermometer points to a temperature. Write the opposite temperature.

11 _____

12 _____

13 _____

14 _____

15 _____

16 _____

17 _____

18 Write the *opposite* temperature for Exercises 4 and 8 above. _____

_____

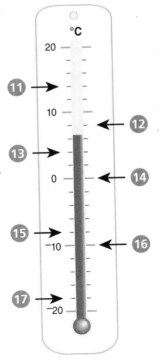

Negative Numbers

Name _____

Understand Number Lines

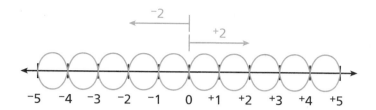

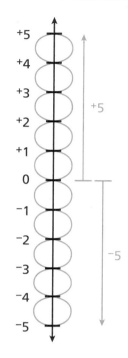

Positive numbers are to the right of, or above, zero.
Negative numbers are to the left of, or below, zero.

The set of **integers** includes all whole numbers (0, 1, 2, 3, 4, ...), and their opposites. Integers represent the *distance* in unit lengths from zero (shown by the numeral), and *direction* from zero (shown by $^+$ or $^-$).

19 What do the loops on each number line show?

_____

20 How do the blue arrows above the horizontal number line show both *direction* and *distance*?

_____

_____

21 How do the blue arrows to the right of the vertical number line both *direction* and *distance*?

_____

_____

22 Are $^+2$ and $^-2$, and $^+5$ and $^-5$ opposite integers? Explain.

_____

_____

23 What do the arrows at the end of each number line mean?

_____

24 Write a three-digit number and its opposite.

_____

Distance and Points on a Number Line

One way to represent distance on a number line is to circle unit lengths. Another way is to mark points. The number lines on this page use tick marks and points to show the origin and unit lengths.

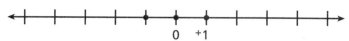

25 One point on each number line is not labeled. Label each point with an integer, and explain why you chose that integer.

_____

_____

26 On each number line, draw a point at each tick mark. Label each point.

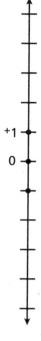

What's the Error?

Dear Math Students,

Today I drew a number line to show the integers from +2 to ⁻2.

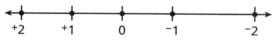

My friends say that I did not draw the number line correctly.

Can you tell me what I did wrong?

Your friend,
Puzzled Penguin

27 Write a response to Puzzled Penguin.

_____

_____

✓ Check Understanding

Give an example of a situation in which you might use a negative number. Explain what 0 would represent in your example.

Interpret a Double Bar Graph

A **double bar graph** uses vertical or horizontal bars to compare data for two groups. This graph shows matinee ticket prices for adults and children at four movie theaters.

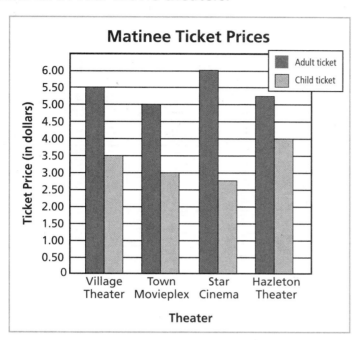

1 At the Hazleton Theater, how much does an adult ticket cost? How much does a child ticket cost?

_____

2 At which theater is the difference between the adult ticket price and the child ticket price greatest? What is the difference in price?

_____

3 Mr. Wong and his three children want to see _Rabbit Robots._ It is playing at both the Village Theater and the Star Cinema. At which theater would their total ticket cost be less? How much less would it be?

_____

4 Mr. and Mrs. Diaz want to take their 7-year-old niece to see _Rabbit Robots._ Would it be less expensive for them to go to the Village Theater or the Star Cinema? How much less?

_____

Make a Double Bar Graph

This table shows the numbers of adults and children who saw *Rabbit Robots* last week at four movie theaters.

5 Make a double bar graph for these data. You will need to choose an appropriate scale and give your graph a title. Be sure to complete the key to show which color represents adults and which represents children.

Last Week's Attendance for *Rabbit Robots*		
Theater	Adults	Children
Village Theater	500	900
Midtown Movies	650	1,100
Star Cinema	300	800
Film World	450	700

6 Write and solve a problem about the information shown in your double bar graph.

Double Bar Graphs and Line Graphs

Name _____

A Double Bar Graph of Fractional Data

Ms. Mason has given two math tests so far this year. This table shows the amount of time four students studied for each test.

Study Time (in hours)		
Student	**Test 1**	**Test 2**
Conor	$\frac{3}{4}$	$1\frac{1}{4}$
Takia	$1\frac{1}{2}$	1
Ahmed	$2\frac{1}{2}$	$1\frac{3}{4}$
Sophia	$\frac{1}{2}$	$2\frac{1}{4}$

7 Make a double bar graph for these data. You will need to choose an appropriate scale, label the vertical axis, and give your graph a title. Be sure to complete the key to show what the two bars represent for each student.

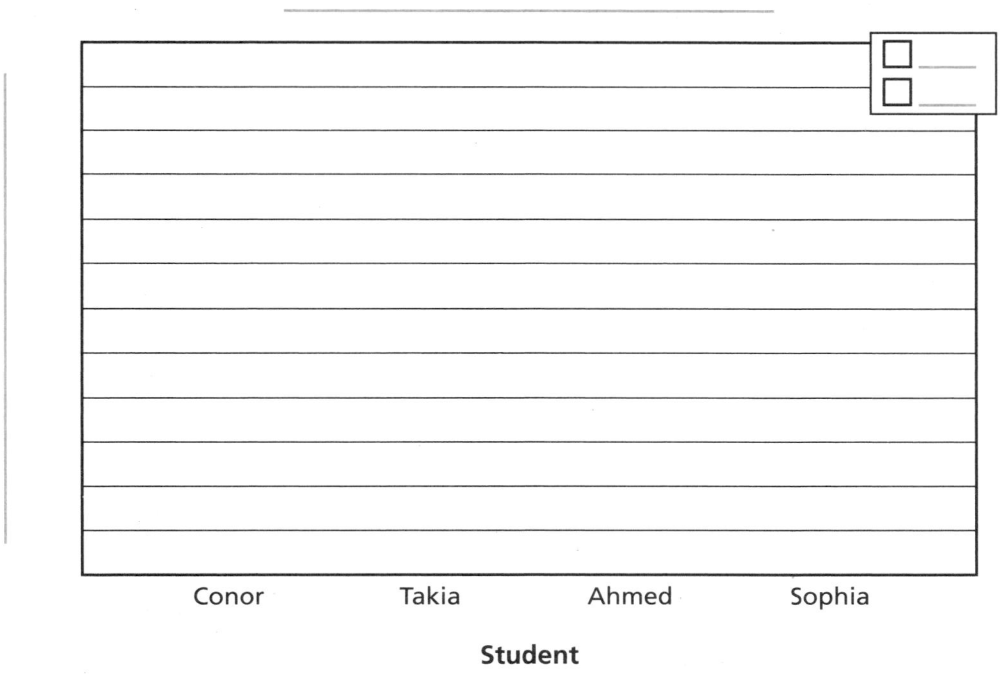

_____

□ _____
□ _____

Conor   Takia   Ahmed   Sophia

Student

8 Write and solve a problem about the information shown in your double bar graph.

_____

_____

_____

Double Bar Graphs and Line Graphs **331**

Interpret a Line Graph

VOCABULARY
line graph

A **line graph** shows how a quantity changes over time. This line graph shows how the total distance Alana ran changed during a 5-mile race.

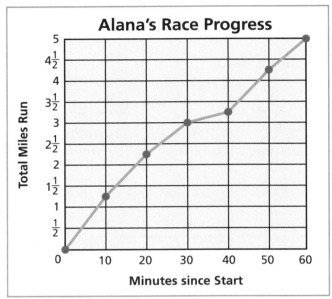

Alana's Race Progress

9 How far did Alana run in the first 20 minutes of the race?

_____

10 How far did she run in the next 20 minutes?

_____

11 During which 10-minute interval did Alana run the greatest distance? How far did she run?

_____

12 During which 10-minute interval did she run the least distance? How far did she run?

_____

13 Use the graph to predict how far Alana had run 15 minutes after the race started. Explain how you made your prediction.

_____

_____

© Houghton Mifflin Harcourt Publishing Company

Double Bar Graphs and Line Graphs

Name _____

Make a Line Graph

Josh earns money by mowing lawns and shoveling snow for his neighbors. He puts some of the money he earns in a savings account.

This table shows the balance in Josh's account on the first day of each month for a sixth-month period.

Josh's Savings Account	
Month	**Balance**
January	$30
February	$40
March	$100
April	$80
May	$150
June	$190

⑭ Make a line graph that shows how Josh's account balance changed over time. You will need to choose an appropriate scale, vertical axis label, and title for your graph.

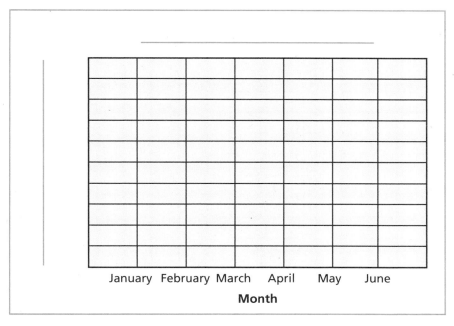

Month

January February March April May June

⑮ Between which two consecutive months (months that occur one after the other) did Josh's account balance increase most? By how much did it increase?

_____

⑯ Between which two consecutive months did Josh's account balance decrease? How is this shown in the graph?

_____

⑰ On a separate sheet of paper, write and solve a problem about the information shown in your line graph.

A Line Graph of Decimal Data

This table shows the cost of the Sunday edition of the Northville Gazette newspaper at 5-year intervals from 1985 to 2015.

Cost of Sunday Paper	
Year	Cost
1985	$0.25
1990	$0.60
1995	$1.30
2000	$1.30
2005	$1.60
2010	$1.75
2015	$1.90

18 Make a line graph that shows how the cost of the Sunday paper changed over time. You will need to choose an appropriate scale, vertical axis label, and title for your graph.

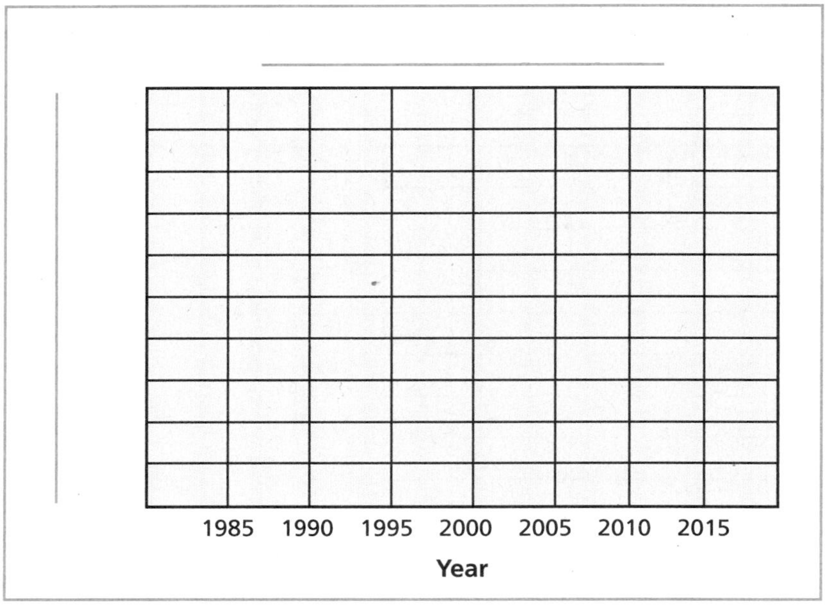

1985 1990 1995 2000 2005 2010 2015

Year

19 The cost of the paper did not change from 1995 to 2000. How is this shown in the graph?

_____

20 Write and solve a problem about the information shown in your line graph.

_____

_____

✓ **Check Understanding**

To show how the data for two groups compare, you can make a

_____. To show how a quantity

changes over time, you can make a _____.

Double Bar Graphs and Line Graphs

Name _____

Take a Survey

Conduct a survey to determine what breakfast foods students in your class prefer. Your teacher will give you a piece of paper with a list of five choices: eggs, cold cereal, oatmeal, pancakes, and other. You and your classmates will each circle your favorite from these five. Keep your choice secret.

VOCABULARY
hypothesis

A **hypothesis** is a statement used as a basis of an investigation.

1 Write a possible hypothesis predicting the results of this survey.

_____

_____

_____

_____

Favorite Breakfast Foods	
Breakfast Food Choice	Tally
Eggs	
Cold cereal	
Oatmeal	
Pancakes	
Other	

2 Collect the ballots and record the results in the frequency chart.

3 Make a bar graph for these data. You will need to choose an appropriate scale and give your graph a title.

4 Does the data support your hypothesis? Explain why or why not.

_____

_____

_____

_____

Number of Students

Eggs   Cold cereal   Oatmeal   Pancakes   Other

Breakfast Food Choice

Testing a Hypothesis

Here's your opportunity to design a study to investigate a question of your choice. Your question should lead to a testable hypothesis.

5 Write a question that can be answered by collecting categorical or numerical data using the people or objects in your classroom.

_____

6 What is your hypothesis relating to this topic's question?

_____

7 How will you collect your data? Describe the procedures in detail.

_____

_____

_____

8 Carry out your investigation. Record and organize the data. Make a table to show your data.

9 What kind of graph will be best to display your data?

_____

10 Draw your graph on a separate sheet of paper.

11 Analyze your results. Do the data support your hypothesis? Explain.

_____

_____

_____

✓ **Check Understanding**

A survey asked students which of the following insects were the most interesting: butterfly, moth, dragonfly, or bumble bee. Write a hypothesis that could be tested by the results of the survey.

Testing a Hypothesis

Name _____

Leveling Out the Data

The **mean** of a set of data is a number that describes the size of each of *n* equal groups made from *n* data values. You can find the mean by adding the values and dividing that sum by the number of values.

1 Davis made 4 clay pots on Friday, 7 clay pots on Saturday, and 4 clay pots on Sunday. What is the mean number of pots he made each day? Make a drawing to show how the pots for each day can be redistributed to find the mean.

_____

2 Serena, Marco, and Ray each have a fish tank. Serena has 5 fish. Marco has 6 fish. Ray has 10 fish. What is the mean number of fish that the three friends have? Make a drawing to show how they can move fish so each person has an equal share.

_____

Calculate the Mean

Find the mean.

Show your work.

3 2, 3, 5, 7, 8   Mean: _____

4 1, 6, 13, 4, 12, 3, 10   Mean: _____

5 29, 35, 18, 62   Mean: _____

6 165, 917, 443, 212, 218   Mean: _____

Word Problems with Mean

**Last week, the town of Midville hosted a county fair.
Solve these problems about the fair.**

7 The Johnson family attended the fair. The ticket prices for the fair are listed below.

Adults	$5.00
Teens (13–18 years old)	$4.00
Children (under 13)	$3.00

There are 2 adults and 2 teens in the Johnson family. What was the mean ticket price for the family?

_____

_____

8 The organizers recorded the attendance each weekday. What was the mean attendance?

Day	Attendance
Monday	874
Tuesday	658
Wednesday	723
Thursday	796
Friday	909

_____

_____

9 Because the fair was so popular, the organizers decided to extend it one more day. On Saturday, 954 people attended the fair. What was the mean attendance over the 6 days?

_____

_____

10 The fair organizers kept track of the high temperature each day. It was 67°F on Monday, 71°F on Tuesday, 75°F on Wednesday, 69°F on Thursday, and 78°F on Friday. What was the mean high temperature during the five days of the fair?

_____

_____

Mean, Median, and Range

Name _____

Find the Median

VOCABULARY
median
range

The **median** of a set of data is the middle value when the values are listed in order from least to greatest or greatest to least.

14, 25, 27, 32, 32
The median is 27.

If there are two middle values, the median is the mean of the two middle values (it is halfway between them).

14, 25, 32, 32
The median is the mean of 25 and 32, which is 28.5.

Solve.

11 Mark's family all bought lunch at the fair. Mark's lunch cost $4.25, his sister's lunch cost $5.76, his brother's lunch cost $4.50, his mom's $6.20, his grandmother's $3.75, and his dad's $6.74. Find the mean and median for the amounts Mark and his family paid for lunch.

mean: _____

median: _____

12 During the first week of the fair, the daily totals of visitors were 425, 556, 249, 425, 624, 780, 658. Find the mean and median for the daily totals of visitors.

mean: _____

median: _____

Find the Range

A **range** is a way to describe data, and is found by subtracting the least (or minimum) number in a set from the greatest (or maximum) number.

For example, in the set of numbers at the right, the greatest number is 28 and the least number is 15. The range of the set of numbers is 13 because $28 - 15 = 13$.

greatest
↓
{16, 28, 17, 20, 15, 23}
↑
least

Find the range of each set of numbers.

13 {7, 5, 5, 1, 9, 4, 5}

range = _____

14 {68, 81, 47, 56, 19, 30}

range = _____

15 {104, 267, 199, 431}

range = _____

Word Problems with Mean, Median, and Range

Solve.   *Show your work.*

16 There was a Guess-Your-Age booth at the fair. One afternoon, the ages of the visitors to the booth were 22, 33, 22, 30, 33, 27, and 22. Find the mean, median, and range of the ages.

mean: _____   median: _____   range: _____

17 One more person came to the booth. His age was 67 years. Find the new mean, median, and range of the visitors' ages.

mean: _____   median: _____   range: _____

Statistics and Bar Graphs

The data in a bar graph can be described in many ways. Some of the ways include finding the mean, median, and range of the data.

Use the bar graph at the right to answer the questions.

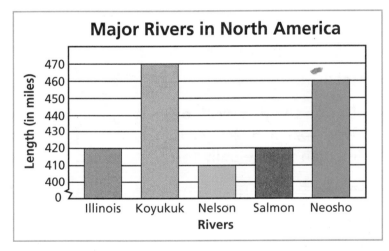

18 How can you tell by looking at the graph that the mean length is greater than 410 miles?

_____

_____

19 Explain how you can find the median simply by looking at the graph.

_____

_____

✓ **Check Understanding**

Which measure or measures of the data—mean, median, or range—would *not* be affected if a river with a length of 450 miles was added to the graph above? _____

The table shows the average monthly temperature for Greensburg.

| Average Monthly Temperature in Greensburg ||
Month	Average Temperature (°C)
January	2
February	7
March	14
April	19

1 Make a line graph to show the average monthly temperature.

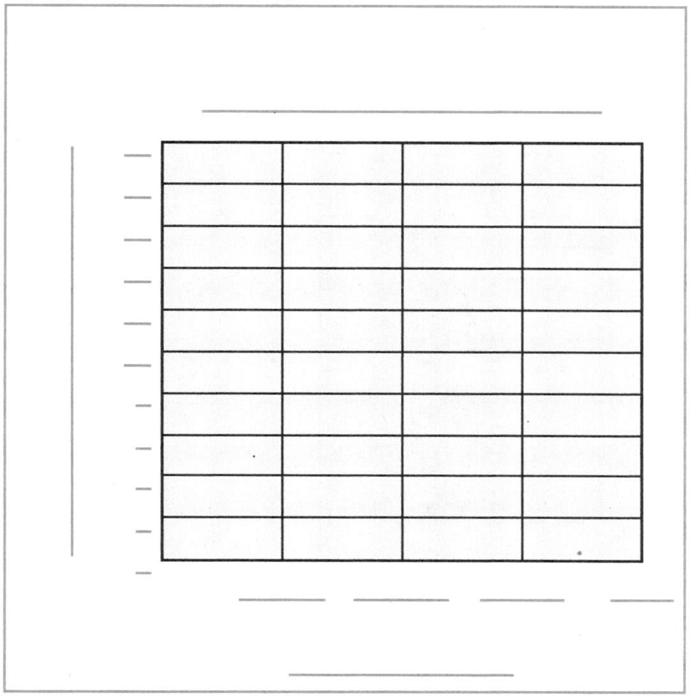

2 Between which consecutive months is the increase in temperature greatest?

_____

3 The highest temperature recorded in Greensburg was 35°C. Write the opposite temperature.

_____

Name _____

Date _____

The graph shows the monthly rainfall (in centimeters) in January and February in three towns.

Monthly Rainfall (cm)		
	January	February
Edgarville	2.5	3
Brownsville	3.75	3.25
Burlington	2.85	3.8

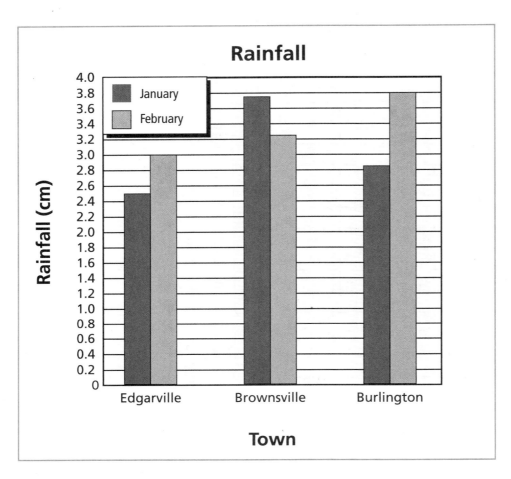

4 What is the mean rainfall for the three towns in January to the nearest centimeter?

_____

5 How much more rainfall did Burlington receive over the two months than Edgarville?

_____

1 Use the numbers to complete the ordered pairs that represent the endpoints of line segment *RT*.

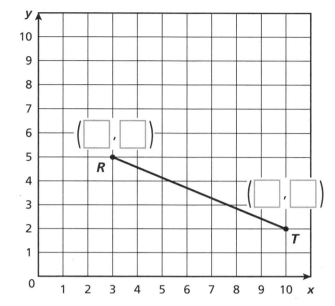

2 Place parentheses in the expression so it simplifies to 30.

$5 \cdot 7 - 3 + 2$

3 Substitute the given value for the variable. Write *true* or *false* for the inequality that results.

$\frac{1}{4} \cdot t \leq 30$

3a. $t = 60$ _____   **3b.** $t = 90$ _____   **3c.** $t = 160$ _____

4 Write $8 \div (7 - 5)$ using words.

5 The lowest point on land is the Dead Sea. It lies 420 meters below sea-level. Which of the following represents the elevation of the Dead Sea? Choose all that apply.

○ ⁻420 meters   ○ 0 meters   ○ 420 meters below sea level

6 Use the Order of Operations to simplify the expression.

6a. $15 + 6 \div 3$ ☐   **6b.** $2 + 5 \cdot 8$ ☐   **6c.** $20 \div (4 + 6)$ ☐

7️⃣ The graph shows the line segment *AB*.

Part A

Write the ordered pairs that represent the endpoints of line segment *AB*.

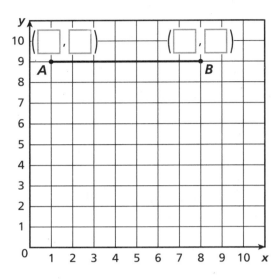

Part B

Explain how subtraction can be used to find the length of line segment *AB*.

8️⃣ For Exercises 8a–8e, select True or False to indicate whether the expression represents multiplying the sum of 8 and 2 by 6.

8a. $8 + 2 \cdot 6$ ○ True   ○ False

8b. $(8 + 2) \cdot 6$ ○ True   ○ False

8c. $8 + (2 \cdot 6)$ ○ True   ○ False

8d. $6 \cdot (8 + 2)$ ○ True   ○ False

8e. $6 \cdot 8 + 2$ ○ True   ○ False

9 Write a letter in each box that shows the expressions in order from least to greatest.

A	B	C	D
$48 \div (4 - 2) + 60 \div 2$	$42 \div 7 - 3 \cdot 2$	$9 + (18 - 3) \div 0.3$	$(1.4 + 0.6) \cdot (2 - 0.4)$

☐ , ☐ , ☐ , ☐

least   greatest

10 Select one expression and one value for the variable that makes the sentence true.

Zeke got 38 when he correctly evaluated the expression ____?____ for ____?____.

Expression	Value of Variable
○ $n \div 2 + 20$	○ $n = 2$
○ $8 + n \cdot 3$	○ $n = 5$
○ $(16 - n) \cdot 4$	○ $n = 10$
○ $40 - (60 \div n)$	○ $n = 12$

11 The table shows rules for two numerical patterns.

Part A

Complete the table by writing the next four terms in each pattern.

Add 5	5				
Add 20	20				

Part B

Describe a relationship between the corresponding pairs in the two patterns.

12 The lake's water level rises 10 centimeters each day. The table shows the total change in water level for 0, 1, 2, and 3 days.

Time (days)	0	1	2	3
Total Change (cm)	0	10	20	30

Part A

Graph the data in the table. Connect the points, and extend the line.

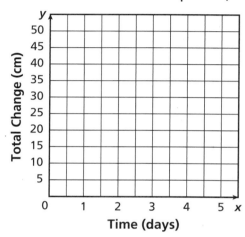

Part B

What total change in water level would you expect after 5 days? Explain your reasoning.

13 For Exercises 13a–13f, choose Yes or No to indicate whether the first step in simplifying the expression is addition.

13a. $6 + 3 - 2 + 1$ ○ Yes   ○ No

13b. $8.5 + 3 \cdot 4 - 2$ ○ Yes   ○ No

13c. $45 \div (5 - 3) + 6$ ○ Yes   ○ No

13d. $40 \div 4 \cdot (2 + 8)$ ○ Yes   ○ No

13e. $45 + 4 - 2 \div 2$ ○ Yes   ○ No

13f. $[25.6 - (4.5 + 2)] \cdot 1.4$ ○ Yes   ○ No

14 Stephen is flying his kite. He lets out 15 feet of string each minute.
Complete the table to show how much string he lets out for 1, 2, and 3
minutes. Then graph the data and connect the points.

Time (minutes)	0			
Length (feet)	0			

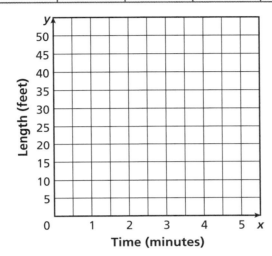

15 Tami measures the total amount of water, in liters, that flows out of
her sink and tub faucets each minute they are running. Describe two
different relationships that the graph displays.

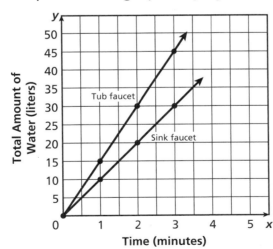

A nature park has two hiking trails. The table shows the amount of time it takes each student to hike each trail.

Hiking Time (in Hours)		
Student	Trail A	Trail B
Frida	$1\frac{1}{2}$	$2\frac{1}{4}$
Noor	$1\frac{3}{4}$	$2\frac{1}{4}$
Shane	2	$2\frac{1}{2}$
Beena	$1\frac{1}{4}$	$1\frac{3}{4}$

16 Make a double bar graph for these data.

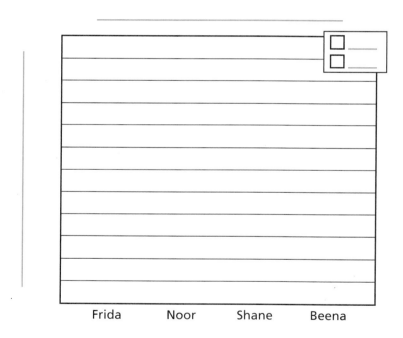

Frida   Noor   Shane   Beena

17 Find the range for the hiking times for Trail A.

_____

18 Find the median for the hiking times for Trail B.

_____

How Far Is It?

Jaime plots landmarks in his town on a coordinate plane. Use the coordinates in the chart to plot the landmarks on your grid paper.

Landmarks

School (2, 10)   Home (10, 12)

Library (5, 3)   Hobby Shop (11, 18)

Gas station (15, 3)   Game Store (18, 9)

Swimming Pool (15, 6)   Sandwich Shop (4, 16)

Park (12, 4)   Bicycle Shop (7, 9)

---

1 Use grid paper to plot and label the landmarks with words or pictures.

2 Name two locations that have the same *x*-coordinate. Explain how to find the distance between the points.

3 Jaime's friend Ryan lives halfway between the library and the gas station. Find the coordinates of the location of Ryan's house. Explain how you found the coordinates.

4 A parallelogram is a quadrilateral with opposite sides of equal length. Name four locations on the coordinate plane that form the vertices of a parallelogram. Use a ruler to verify that the lengths of the opposite sides of the parallelogram are equal.

5 Sometimes after school, Jaime jogs on a rectangular path that takes him past the library, the bicycle shop, the sandwich shop, and then back to the school. Draw Jaime's rectangular path on the coordinate plane and write the coordinates of the vertices of the rectangle. Then find the total distance Jaime jogs. Explain how you found the total distance.

_____

_____

_____

6 Suppose Jaime is at the library. He wants to get something to eat and then do something fun before going home. Connect points to show a path Jaime can take on the grid lines. Write an expression to represent the units between each landmark on the path. Simplify your expression to find the total distance of the path.

_____

_____

_____

7 Suppose Jaime is at home. Plan a route in which Jaime visits two landmarks and then returns home. Write an expression that represents the units between each landmark on the path using a variable for the unknown units. Then choose a scale for the grid and evaluate the expression using that scale.

_____

_____

_____

_____

Dear Family:

Your child is learning to convert units of measurement for length, liquid volume, and weight. Liquid volume is a measure of the amount of liquid in a container. It is measured in units such as liters or quarts.

Volume is a measure of the space that a three-dimensional figure, such as a box, occupies. This is a new topic at this grade level.

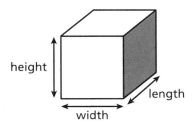

Your child will learn the underlying concepts of volume as well as multiply the three dimensions of a rectangular prism, length × width × height to find its volume. Volume is measured in cubic units, such as cubic meters or cubic feet.

Your child will also learn about units of weight and mass. Two objects with the same volume can have very different masses— for example, iron and wood. Weight is a measure of the pull of gravity on these objects: an object made of iron weighs more than that same object made of wood. Weight is different on Earth than on the moon, but mass always stays the same.

Your child will also learn that attributes belonging to a category of two-dimensional figures also belong to all subcategories of that category. Students then learn to classify two-dimensional figures in a hierarchy based on properties.

Your child will also develop and use formulas for finding area starting with rectangles and progressing to triangles, parallelograms, regular polygons, and complex figures.

Finally your child will expand his or her earlier understanding of three-dimensional figures to include spheres, cylinders, cones, prisms, and pyramids. These lessons guide your child in an investigation of the attributes of these shapes and enable them to name a shape based on those attributes. Later lessons will examine nets, a two-dimensional figure that can be folded to form the surface of a three-dimensional figure. Your child's understanding of the attributes of the three-dimensional figures mentioned above will allow him or her to identify what object a net represents and also use the net to calculate surface area of the object.

If you have any questions or comments, please contact me.

Sincerely,
Your child's teacher

Estimada familia:

Su niño está aprendiendo a convertir unidades de medida de longitud, volumen de líquidos y peso. El volumen de un líquido es la medida de la cantidad de líquido en un recipiente. Se mide en unidades tales como litros o cuartos.

El volumen es la medida del espacio que una figura tridimensional, tal como una caja, ocupa. Este es un tema nuevo en este grado.

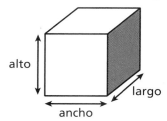

Su niño aprenderá los conceptos subyacentes de volumen, así como a multiplicar las tres medidas de un prisma rectangular: largo × ancho × alto, para hallar su volumen. El volumen se mide en unidades cúbicas, tales como metros cúbicos o pies cúbicos.

Su niño también aprenderá acerca de unidades de peso y de masa. Dos objetos con el mismo volumen pueden tener masas muy diferentes, por ejemplo, el hierro y la madera. El peso es la medida de la fuerza de gravedad ejercida sobre esos objetos: un objeto de hierro pesa más que el mismo objeto hecho de madera. El peso en la Tierra es diferente que el peso en la Luna, pero la masa siempre es la misma.

Su niño también aprenderá que los atributos que pertenecen a una categoría de figuras bidimensionales, también pertenecen a todas las subcategorías de esa categoría. Luego, los niños aprenderán a clasificar figuras bidimensionales usando una jerarquía basada en las propiedades.

Su niño también desarrollará y usará fórmulas para encontrar el área comenzando con rectángulos y progresando a triángulos, paralelogramos, polígonos regulares y figuras complejas.

Finalmente, su niño ampliará su comprensión de figuras tridimensionales incluyendo esferas, cilindros, conos, prismas y pirámides. Estas lecciones guían a su niño en una investigación de los atributos de estas figuras y les permiten nombrar una figura basada en esos atributos. En lecciones posteriores estudiarán las plantillas, una figura bidimensional que se puede doblar para formar la superficie de una figura tridimensional. La comprensión de su niño de los atributos de las figuras tridimensionales mencionadas anteriormente le permitirá identificar qué objeto representa una plantilla y también usar la plantilla para calcular el área total del objeto.

Si tiene alguna pregunta o algún comentario, por favor comuníquese conmigo.

Atentamente,
El maestro de su niño

Metric Units of Length

acute
triangle

base of a prism

area

base of a
triangle

base of a
parallelogram

closed shape

One of two congruent parallel faces of a prism.

Example:

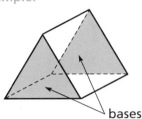

bases

A triangle with three acute angles.

Examples:

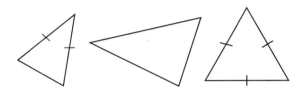

The side of a triangle that is perpendicular to its height.

Example:

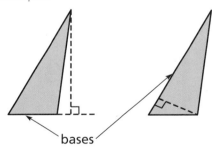

bases

The total number of unit squares that cover a figure. A unit square has an area of 1 square unit.

Example:
Area = 3 cm × 5 cm = 15 sq cm

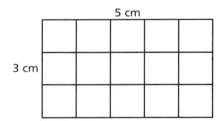

5 cm

3 cm

A shape that starts and ends at the same point.

Examples:

A side of a parallelogram that is perpendicular to its height.

Example:

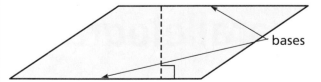

bases

complex figure

cone

composite solid

congruent

concave
polygon

convex polygon

A three-dimensional figure that has one flat base that is a circle.

cone

A figure made up of two or more basic shapes.

Example:

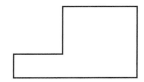

This figure is made up of a small rectangle and a large square.

Having the same size and shape.

A solid figure made by combining two or more basic solid figures.

Example:

The composite solid on the left below is composed of two rectangular prisms, as shown on the right.

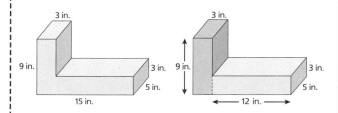

A polygon that is not concave. All the inside angles of a convex polygon have a measure less than 180°.

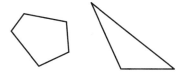

A polygon for which you can connect two points inside the polygon with a segment that passes outside the polygon. A concave polygon has a "dent."

Examples:

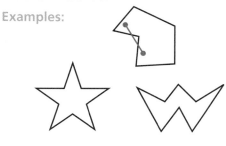

cube	dimensions
cubic unit	edge
cylinder	equilateral triangle

The length, width, or height of a figure.

A three-dimensional figure that is made of 6 square congruent faces.

A line segment where two faces of a three-dimensional figure meet.

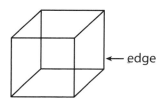
← edge

The volume of a unit cube. A cubic unit is a unit for measuring volume.

A triangle with three sides of the same length.

Example:

A three-dimensional figure that has two flat, congruent bases that are circles.

cylinder

face

height of a triangle

frequency table

isosceles triangle

height of a parallelogram

length

The measure of a line segment that extends from a vertex to one side of the triangle (or an extension of that side) and forms a right angle with that side (or its extension).

Examples:

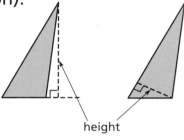

A flat surface of a three-dimensional figure.

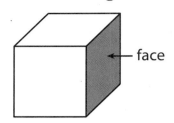

A triangle with at least two sides of the same length.

Examples:

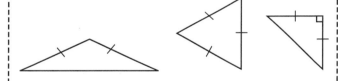

A table that shows how many times each outcome, item, or category occurs.

Example:

Outcome	Number of Students
1	6
2	3
3	5
4	4
5	2
6	5

Measurement of how wide, tall, or long something is.

A measure of a line segment that is perpendicular to the base of the parallelogram.

Examples:

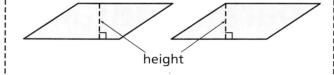

line plot	obtuse triangle
mile (mi)	one-dimensional
net	open shape

A triangle with an obtuse angle.

Examples:

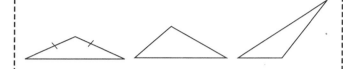

A diagram that uses a number line to show the frequency of data.

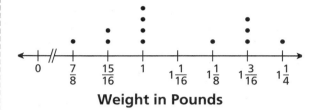

Weight in Pounds

Having a single dimension. Length is one-dimensional.

Example:

1 cm

A U.S. customary unit of length equal to 5,280 feet or 1,760 yards.

A shape that does not start and end at the same point.

Examples:

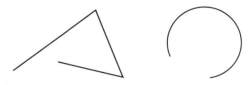

A flat or plane figure that can be cut and folded to form a three-dimensional figure.

parallelogram	polygon
perimeter	prism
perpendicular	pyramid

A closed two-dimensional shape made from line segments that do not cross each other.

Examples:

A quadrilateral with two pairs of parallel sides.

Examples:

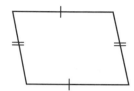

A three-dimensional figure that has two congruent opposite faces that are polygons. The shape of the base is used to name the prism.

Examples:

rectangular prism   pentagonal prism

The distance around a figure.

Example:
Perimeter = 2 · 3 cm + 2 · 5 cm = 16 cm

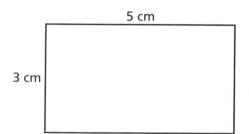

A three-dimensional figure that has a polygon-shaped base and triangular faces that meet at a point. The shape of the base is used to name the pyramid.

Examples:

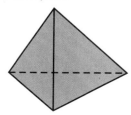 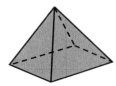

triangular pyramid   rectangular pyramid

Two lines or line segments are perpendicular if they cross or meet to form 90° angles (square corners).

Examples:

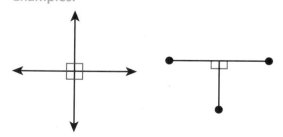

quadrilateral

regular polygon

rectangle

rhombus

rectangular prism

right triangle

A polygon in which all sides and all angles are congruent.

Examples:

 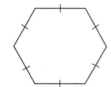

A closed two-dimensional shape with four straight sides.

Examples:

A parallelogram with four congruent sides.

Examples:

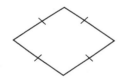

A parallelogram with four right angles.

Examples:

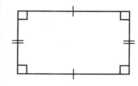

A triangle with a right angle.

Examples:

A solid figure with two rectangular bases that are congruent and parallel.

Example:

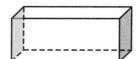

scalene triangle	surface area
sphere	three-dimensional
square	ton (T)

The total area of the faces or curved surfaces of a three-dimensional figure.

A triangle with no sides of the same length.

Examples:

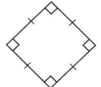

Having three dimensions, usually length, width, and height.

Example:

1 cm
1 cm   1 cm

A three-dimensional figure made up of points that are the same distance from its center. It has no flat surfaces.

Example:

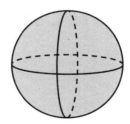

A customary unit of weight that equals 2,000 pounds.

A rectangle with four congruent sides. (Or, a rhombus with four right angles.)

Examples:

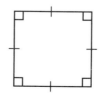 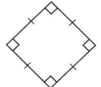

triangular prism	unit cube
trapezoid	vertex (vertices) of a 2-D figure
two-dimensional	vertex (vertices) of a 3-D figure

A cube with side lengths of 1 unit.

A three-dimensional figure that has two congruent parallel bases that are triangles.

Example:

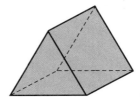

In a two-dimensional figure, the point at which two line segments or two rays meet at an endpoint.

Example:

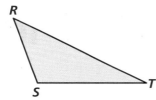

Line segments *RT* and *ST* meet at vertex *T*.

A quadrilateral with exactly one pair of parallel sides.

Examples:

In a three-dimensional figure, the point at which three or more edges meet at a point.

Examples:

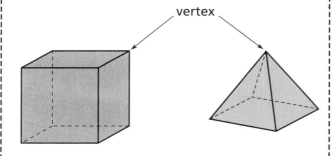

Having two dimensions, usually length and width.

Example:

volume

A measure of the amount of space occupied by a solid figure. Volume is measured in cubic units.

Name _____

Convert Units of Length

A meter is the basic unit of metric length. This chart shows the relationship between meters and other metric units of length.

Metric Units of Length	
1 **dekameter (dam)** = 10 meters	1 meter = 0.1 dekameter
1 **hectometer (hm)** = 100 meters	1 meter = 0.01 hectometer
1 **kilometer (km)** = 1,000 meters	1 meter = 0.001 kilometer
1 meter = 10 **decimeters (dm)**	0.1 meter = 1 decimeter
1 meter = 100 **centimeters (cm)**	0.01 meter = 1 centimeter
1 meter = 1,000 **millimeters (mm)**	0.001 meter = 1 millimeter

Example 1 **Convert to a Smaller Unit**	Example 2 **Convert to a Larger Unit**
2 km = _____ m	50 cm = _____ m
Multiply because we will need more of the smaller units.	Divide because we will need fewer of the larger units.
Convert kilometers to meters.	**Convert centimeters to meters.**
Multiply by 1,000 because 1 km = 1,000 m.	Divide by 100 because 100 cm = 1 m.
2 km = <u>2,000</u> m (1,000 × 2 = 2,000)	50 cm = <u>0.5</u> m (50 ÷ 100 = 0.5)

Complete.

1. 15 m = _____ mm

2. 0.36 km = _____ m

3. 2,040 mm = _____ m

4. 9.2 m = _____ cm

5. 877 cm = _____ m

6. 31 mm = _____ m

7. 2.39 m = _____ cm

8. 450 m = _____ km

9. 4,850 mm = _____ m

10. 57 m = _____ km

11. 8.6 km = _____ m

12. 41 cm = _____ m

Solving Problems with Hidden Information

13 Jenny knitted a scarf that was 2.6 meters long. She made an identical scarf every month for 2 years. How many centimeters of scarf had she knitted all together by the end of 2 years?

   a. How many meters of scarf did Jenny knit in 1 month? _____

   b. For how many months did Jenny knit? _____

   c. How many scarves did she knit during that time? _____

   d. How many meters is that? _____

   e. How many centimeters of scarf did Jenny knit in 2 years? _____

Solve. Check that your answer is reasonable.   *Show your work.*

14 Natasha ran 3.1 kilometers. Tonya ran 4 meters more than half as far as Natasha. How many meters did Tonya run?

_____

15 A European swallow flies about 11 meters in 1 second. How many kilometers could it fly in 15 minutes?

_____

16 Allie needs 65 centimeters of fabric for the pillow she is making. The fabric costs $4.20 for a meter and the stuffing for the pillow costs 79¢. How much will it cost her to make the pillow?

_____

17 Leon is building a square picture frame. The side of the frame is 345 millimeters long. If a meter of wood costs $7, how much will the wood he needs cost?

_____

Metric Units of Length

Solving Problems with Hidden Information (continued)

Solve. Estimate to check if your answer is reasonable.

Show your work.

18 Pascal wants to ride his bike to and from school 3 days a week. His house is 2.58 kilometers from his school. How many meters will he ride in 7 weeks?

_____

19 If Sabrina's hair grows 1.1 centimeters every month, how many meters could her hair grow over 5 years?

_____

What's the Error?

Dear Math Students,

I want to build a fence around my rectangular garden. My garden is 675 centimeters long and 225 centimeters wide. The fencing costs $3 for every meter of fencing.

This is how I found the cost of the fencing.
Am I correct?

6.75 m

+ 2.25 m
_____
9.00

$3 × 9 = $27

Your friend,
Puzzled Penguin

20 Write a response to Puzzled Penguin.

_____

_____

_____

_____

Multistep Problem Solving

Solve. Check that your answer is reasonable.

Show your work.

21 Mai has a piece of cloth that is 8.35 meters long. How many 15-centimeter pieces can she cut from the cloth? How much will be left over?

_____

22 On the first day of her 5-day trip, Miss Gordon drove 435 kilometers in 5.3 hours. On each of the next three days, she drove 80.78 kilometers in 65 minutes. On the fifth day, she drove 880 meters. How many kilometers did she drive in all?

_____

23 Paula's painting has a perimeter of 1.47 meters. She wants to put ribbon around the edge. If the ribbon comes in pieces that are 25 centimeters long, how many pieces of ribbon does she need to go all the way around her painting?

_____

24 Mattie is making a collar for her dog. She needs to buy some chain, a clasp, and a name tag. She wants the chain to be 40 centimeters long. One meter of chain costs $9.45. The clasp is $1.29 and the name tag is $3.43. How much will it cost to make the collar? Estimate to check if your answer is reasonable.

_____

Estimate: _____

25 Cam rode her bike 5 times as far as Dante did. Dante rode 187 meters farther than Michael did. Cam rode 15.25 kilometers. How many meters did Michael ride?

_____

✓**Check Understanding**

Explain how you got your answer to Problem 25.

Metric Units of Length

Convert Units

VOCABULARY
mile (mi)

Customary Units of Length
1 foot (ft) = 12 inches (in.)
1 yard (yd) = 3 feet = 36 inches
1 mile (mi) = 1,760 yards = 5,280 feet

Example 1 **Convert to a Smaller Unit**	Example 2 **Convert to a Larger Unit**
15 yd = _____ ft	48 in. = _____ ft
Multiply because we will need more of the smaller units.	Divide because we will need fewer of the larger units.
Convert yards to feet.	**Convert inches to feet.**
Multiply by 3 because 1 yd = 3 ft.	Divide by 12 because 12 in. = 1 ft.
15 yd = ___45___ ft (3 × 15 = 45)	48 in. = ___4___ ft (48 ÷ 12 = 4)

Complete.

1. 24 in. = _____ ft

2. 24 ft = _____ yd

3. 12 ft = _____ in.

4. _____ ft = $1\frac{1}{2}$ yd

5. _____ ft = 6 yd

6. _____ ft = $\frac{1}{2}$ mi

7. _____ yd = 3 mi

8. _____ ft = 54 in.

9. _____ yd = 144 in.

10. $2\frac{1}{2}$ yd = _____ in.

Calculate Perimeter

Calculate the perimeter of each figure in feet.

11.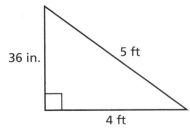

36 in.   5 ft   4 ft

_____

12.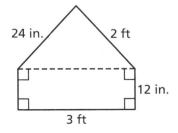

24 in.   2 ft   12 in.   3 ft

_____

Solve Multistep Problems

Solve. Check that your answer is reasonable.   *Show your work.*

13 Nick needs 65 yards of wire for a project. If the wire is only sold on spools which hold 6 feet of wire, how many spools will he need?

_____

14 Jessi has 9 feet of blue fabric. To finish making her costume she needs one third of that amount of red fabric. The fabric store sells fabric by the yard. How much fabric does Jessi need to buy?

_____

15 Jay runs $1\frac{1}{2}$ miles at track practice. Teddy runs the 100-yard dash, and Cadi runs half as far as Jay. How many yards do they run all together?

_____

16 Kelly is hanging shelves in her closet. She can buy shelves for $1.25 a foot. Kelly buys one 5-foot shelf and a shelf that measures 24 inches. The rest of her materials cost $90. How much change will she get it she pays with $100?

_____

17 Paula ran 24 feet with the football and then passed it 15 feet to Newt. Newt ran 70 yards for a touchdown. What was the total number of feet the ball traveled?

_____

18 Patrick bought 54 inches of material that costs $3.40 for one yard. What change did he get if he paid for the material with a twenty-dollar bill?

_____

✓ **Check Understanding**

Would you divide or multiply to convert feet to yards? Explain.

Customary Units of Length

Discuss Perimeter and Area

Perimeter is the distance around a figure.

Area is the total number of unit squares that cover a figure. A unit square has an area of 1 square unit.

Rectangle A

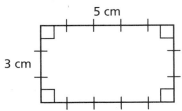

Rectangle B

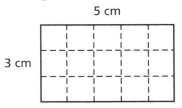

$P = 3 \text{ cm} + 5 \text{ cm} + 3 \text{ cm} + 5 \text{ cm} = 16 \text{ cm}$ $A = 3 \text{ cm} \times 5 \text{ cm} = 15 \text{ sq cm}$

Formula: _____   Formula: _____

Discuss Fractional Side Lengths

To find the area of a rectangle with fractional side lengths, use the same method you use to find the area of a rectangle with whole-number side lengths.

Rectangle C

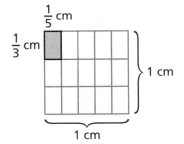

Rectangle D

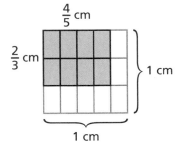

$A = 1$ of 15 equal parts

$A = \frac{1}{3} \text{ cm} \times \frac{1}{5} \text{ cm} = \frac{1}{15} \text{ sq cm}$

$A = \text{eight } \frac{1}{15}\text{'s}$

$A = \frac{2}{3} \text{ cm} \times \frac{4}{5} \text{ cm} = \frac{8}{15} \text{ sq cm}$

Find the perimeter of each green rectangle shown above. Express your answer as a mixed number.

1 Rectangle C: _____   2 Rectangle D: _____

3 Discuss how finding the perimeter of a rectangle with fractional side lengths is the same as and different from finding the perimeter of a rectangle with whole-number side lengths.

Analyze Area Models with Fractional Side Lengths

Solve.

4 Shade and label the model to show the area of a $\frac{1}{2}$ mi by $\frac{1}{4}$ mi rectangle. Describe what your model shows and then find the area numerically.

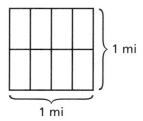

1 mi

1 mi

_____
_____
_____
_____
_____

5 Shade the model to show the area of a $\frac{1}{2}$ mi by $\frac{3}{4}$ mi rectangle. Describe what your model shows and then find the area numerically.

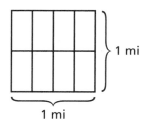

1 mi

1 mi

_____
_____
_____
_____
_____

Find an Unknown Side Length

6 What is the length of a rectangle with a width of 27 feet and an area of 918 square feet?

_____

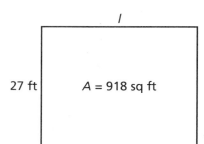

_l_

27 ft   _A_ = 918 sq ft

Name _____

Practice with Area

Find the perimeter and the area of the rectangle. When possible, express your answer as a whole or mixed number.

7

$P =$ _____

$A =$ _____

8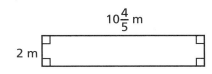

$P =$ _____

$A =$ _____

9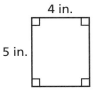

$P =$ _____

$A =$ _____

10

$P =$ _____

$A =$ _____

Find the side length of the rectangle.

11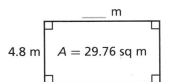

12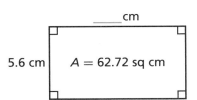

13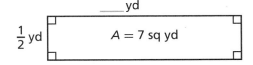

14

Solve Real World Problems

Solve. Express fractions greater than 1 as a mixed number.   *Show your work.*

15 Brian was tiling a patio and ran out of tiles. The width of the remaining area is $\frac{2}{3}$ yard. The length of the remaining area is 4 yards. What is the area Brian has left to tile?

_____

16 Rylee knows that the area for the face-painting station is 166 square feet. She knows that the length of the rectangular area is 12 feet. How wide is the area?

_____

17 Coby needs to know the area and perimeter of his farm property. The length of his property is $\frac{1}{12}$ mile and the width is $\frac{3}{8}$ mile. What is the area? What is the perimeter?

_____

18 The area for the dance floor is 45 square feet, and one side is 8 feet. What is the length of the other side?

_____

19 Margo wants new carpet and a new wallpaper border for her bedroom. The room is 5.4 meters long and $4\frac{7}{8}$ meters wide. About how many square meters of carpet will she need? About how many meters of wallpaper border will she need?

_____

20 Tomas has a garden with a length of 2.45 meters and a width of $\frac{5}{8}$ meter. Use benchmarks to estimate the area and perimeter of the garden.

_____

✓ Check Understanding

Draw a rectangle and use it to explain how the formula for the perimeter of a rectangle and the formula for the area of a rectangle are alike and how they are different.

Name _____

Describe a Cube

VOCABULARY
face
edge
unit cube
cubic unit
volume

Use the cube to answer the questions below.

1 How many **faces** does a cube have? _____

2 How many **edges** does a cube have? _____

Write *true* **or** *false* **for each statement.**

3 All the edges of a cube are the same length. _____

4 All the faces of a cube are the same size squares. _____

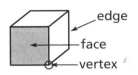

Explore Volume

A **unit cube** is a cube with each edge 1 unit long. The volume of a unit cube is 1 **cubic unit**. The **volume** of an object can be measured by filling it with unit cubes without any gaps or overlaps.

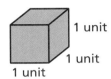

Cut out the nets on page 364A. Fold each of the nets to make an open-ended prism. Fill the prisms with 1-cm cubes leaving no spaces.

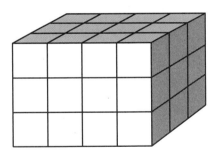

5 Number of cubes: _____

6 Volume: _____

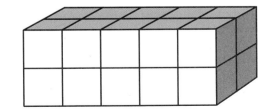

7 Number of cubes: _____

8 Volume: _____

Unit Cubes and Volume

Find the number of unit cubes and the volume.

9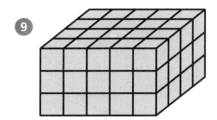

10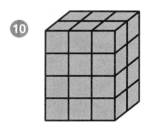

11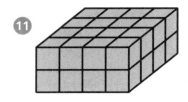

Number of unit cubes: _____

Volume: _____

Number of cubes: _____

Volume: _____

Number of unit cubes: _____

Volume: _____

What's the Error?

Dear Math Students,

This drawing of a cube appears
to have a volume of 19 cubic units
but, when I built it, I used 27 cubes.
What did I do wrong?

Your Friend,
Puzzled Penguin

12 Write a response to Puzzled Penguin.

_____

_____

_____

_____

✓ Check Understanding

The number of unit cubes it takes to fill a prism with no

gaps or overlaps is equal to the _____.

Explore Layers

VOCABULARY
rectangular prism

You can use layers of cubes to build **rectangular prisms**.

Each layer of these rectangular prisms is 4 cubes by 2 cubes. How many cubes make up each prism?

1 layer

_____

2 layers	3 layers	4 layers	5 layers	6 layers
_____	_____	_____	_____	_____

The volume of a prism is the number of cubes needed to build the prism. Volume is recorded in cubic units.

Write the volume of the prism in cubic units.

1. 1 layer: $4 \times 2 \times 1 =$ _____ cubic units

2. 2 layers: $4 \times 2 \times 2 =$ _____ cubic units

3. 3 layers: $4 \times 2 \times 3 =$ _____ cubic units

4. 4 layers: $4 \times 2 \times 4 =$ _____ cubic units

5. 5 layers: $4 \times 2 \times 5 =$ _____ cubic units

6. 6 layers: $4 \times 2 \times 6 =$ _____ cubic units

Calculate Volume

Complete the table.

Prism	length (*l*)	width (*w*)	height (*h*)	(length × width) × height (*l* × *w*) × *h*	volume (*V*)
7 5 ft, 4 ft, 7 ft	7 ft	4 ft	5 ft	(7 × 4) × 5	140 cu ft
8 10 cm, 15 cm, 6 cm					
9 4 m, 4 m, 12 m					
10 8 in., 4 in., 5 in.					
11 7 cm, 10 cm, 15 cm					
12 6 in., 6 in., 6 in.					

> ✓ **Check Understanding**
>
> Explain how the dimensions of a rectangular prism are related to its volume.

Name _____

Develop a Formula

1 What is the volume of this rectangular prism?

_____

2 How do you find the area of a rectangle?

_____

3 How do you find the volume of a rectangular prism?

_____

4 How is finding volume different from finding area?

_____

5 Write a formula for finding the volume of any rectangular prism.

Volume = _____

6 This ice cube is shaped like a cube. Its edge lengths are 2 cm. What is the volume of this ice cube? Write a formula for finding the volume of any cube.

_____

_____

Find an Unknown Edge

7 Raul is building a planter in the shape of a rectangular prism. It has a length of 4 feet and a height of 2 feet. How wide should it be to hold 24 cubic feet of soil? Explain how you found your answer.

_____

_____

_____

_____

_____

　　　　　　　　Introduce Volume Formulas **367**

Practice

Write a numerical expression for the volume. Then calculate the volume.

8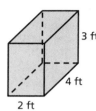

Expression: _____

Volume: _____

9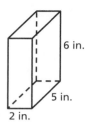

Expression: _____

Volume: _____

10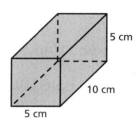

Expression: _____

Volume: _____

Find the unknown dimension or volume of each rectangular prism.

11 V = 120 cu m

l = 4 m

w = _____

h = 5 m

12 V = 120 cu in.

l = _____

w = 4 in.

h = 3 in

13 V = _____

l = 7 cm

w = 6 cm

h = 7 cm

Write an equation. Then solve.

14 A box shaped like a rectangular prism is 2 m long, 2 m wide, and has a height of 3 m. What is the volume of the box?

_____

15 Fred's dog crate is 42 inches long, 24 inches wide, and has a height of 30 inches. What is the volume of the crate?

_____

16 The cargo hold of a truck has a height of 3 yards and is 5 yards wide. The volume of the cargo hold is listed as 240 cubic yards. What is the length of the cargo hold?

_____

 Check Understanding

Draw two identical rectangular prisms and use your drawings to explain the two formulas for volume and how they relate to each other.

Introduce Volume Formulas

Name _____

Compare Length, Area, and Volume

VOCABULARY
length
one-dimensional
two-dimensional
three-dimensional

Length tells how wide, tall, or long something is. Finding length requires one measurement. Length is **one-dimensional** and is measured in linear units.

Area tells how much surface a figure covers. Finding the area of a rectangle requires two linear measurements. Area is **two-dimensional** and is measured in square units.

Volume tells how much space an object occupies. Finding the volume of a rectangular prism requires three linear measurements. Volume is **three-dimensional** and is measured in cubic units.

To answer the question, tell if you need to measure for length, area, or volume. Then write the number of measurements you need to make.

Length |—| 1 cm

Area   [square] 1 cm / 1 cm

Volume   [cube] 1 cm / 1 cm / 1 cm

1 How much water is in a swimming pool? _____

2 How tall are you? _____

3 How much carpet is needed for a floor? _____

4 How far is it from a doorknob to the floor? _____

5 How much sand is in a sandbox? _____

6 How much wallpaper is needed for one wall? _____

7 How long is a string? _____

8 How much space is there inside a refrigerator? _____

Solve Real World Problems

Solve. If possible, write the answer as a whole or mixed number.

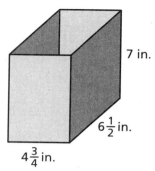

7 in.

$6\frac{1}{2}$ in.

$4\frac{3}{4}$ in.

9 Soledad has a storage box. The box is $6\frac{1}{2}$ inches long, $4\frac{3}{4}$ inches wide, and 7 inches tall. She wants to run a border around the top of the box. How much border does she need?

10 The refrigerator is $5\frac{2}{3}$ feet tall, $2\frac{2}{7}$ feet wide, and $2\frac{1}{4}$ feet deep. How much space does the refrigerator take up on the floor?

11 Melissa is stacking storage cubes in a crate. The bottom of the crate is 8 inches by 12 inches. The volume of the crate is 768 cu inches. If a storage cube has a length of 4 inches, how many storage cubes will fit in the crate?

12 Reed has a lawn mowing service and charges $1.00 for mowing a section of lawn that measures 15 square yards. On Saturday he mows 5 lawns that are each $21\frac{3}{4}$ yards by 27 yards. How much money does Reed earn on Saturday?

13 Parker builds a planter in the shape of a rectangular prism that is 6 feet wide, 3 feet deep, and 2 feet tall. How much soil will he need to fill it?

14 A box is a rectangular prism with a square base. The volume is 972 cubic cm, and the area of the square base is 81 square cm. What is the height of the box?

✓ Check Understanding

Explain how you found the answer to Problem 14.

Relate Length, Area, and Volume

Name _____

Analyze a Composite Solid Figure

A **composite solid** can be made by putting together two or more rectangular prisms. To find the volume of such a composite solid, divide it into individual prisms. Use the formula $V = l \cdot w \cdot h$ to find the volume of each individual prism, and then add the volumes to find the total volume.

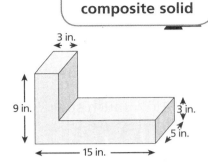

To find the volume, you can decompose the solid into different rectangular prisms.

1 Find the volume of the blue rectangular prism first.

$V_1 =$ _____ × _____ × _____ = _____ cubic inches

$V_2 =$ _____ × _____ × _____ = _____ cubic inches

Total volume = _____ + _____ = _____ cubic inches

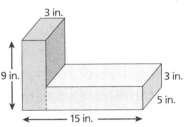

2 Find the volume of the blue rectangular prism first.

$V_1 =$ _____ × _____ × _____ = _____ cubic inches

$V_2 =$ _____ × _____ × _____ = _____ cubic inches

Total volume = _____ + _____ = _____ cubic inches

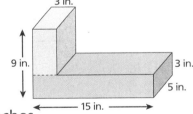

3 Discuss Compare your answers to Problems 1 and 2. What conclusion or conclusions can you make?

Practice

Find the volume of each composite solid figure.

 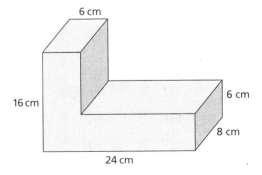

$V =$ _____

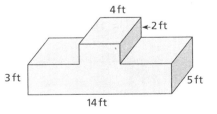

$V =$ _____

Real World Problems

6 This building consists of two rectangular prisms—a small space for offices and an attached larger space for warehouse storage.

How much space does the building take up?

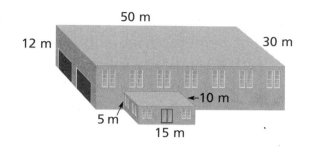

_____

7 The size of a furnace depends on the volume of air in a building. A heating contractor must size a furnace for the three-unit apartment building shown in the sketch at the right.

What is the volume of air in the building?

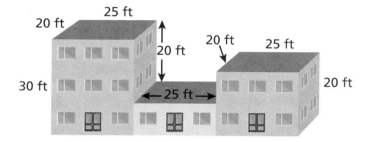

_____

8 An in-ground swimming pool often has steps that are made from poured concrete. In the sketch of the steps at the right, the steps are identical, each measuring 18 inches from side to side, 12 inches from front to back, and 8 inches tall.

Calculate the amount of concrete that is needed to form the steps.

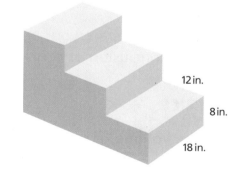

_____

✓ Check Understanding

Draw line segments to show the way you decomposed the pool steps in Problem 8.

Use a formula to write an equation and calculate the volume of the figure.

1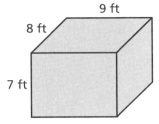

8 ft   9 ft

7 ft

2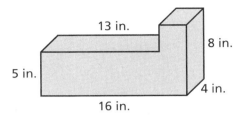

13 in.

5 in.   8 in.

16 in.   4 in.

_____   _____

Use a formula to write an equation and solve the problem.   *Show your work.*

3 Grayson bought a rectangular waste basket that is
$1\frac{1}{2}$ feet long, $\frac{3}{4}$ foot wide, and 2 feet high.
Find the volume of the waste basket.

_____

4 A sign is $4\frac{1}{2}$ feet wide and $5\frac{1}{4}$ feet long.
Find the area of the surface of the sign.

_____

5 Each cube in the rectangular prism is
one cubic centimeter. Find the number of
cubes and the volume.

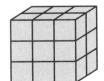

_____

Name   Date

Multiply.

1   70
      $\times$ 3

2   42
      $\times$ 5

3   300
      $\times$ 8

4   670
      $\times$ 5

5   404
      $\times$ 7

6   348
      $\times$ 6

7   918
      $\times$ 4

8   5,000
      $\times$ 6

9   6,003
      $\times$ 9

10   9,012
      $\times$ 5

11   4,882
      $\times$ 8

12   60
      $\times$ 50

13   84
      $\times$ 40

14   68
      $\times$ 31

15   58
      $\times$ 33

Liquid Volume

A liter is the basic unit of metric liquid volume. This chart shows the relationship between liters and other metric units of liquid volume.

Metric Units of Liquid Volume	
1 dekaliter (daL) = 10 liters	1 liter = 0.1 dekaliter
1 hectoliter (hL) = 100 liters	1 liter = 0.01 hectoliter
1 kiloliter (kL) = 1,000 liters	1 liter = 0.001 kiloliter
1 liter = 10 deciliters (dL)	0.1 liter = 1 deciliter
1 liter = 100 centiliters (cL)	0.01 liter = 1 centiliter
1 liter = 1,000 milliliters (mL)	0.001 liter = 1 milliliter

Example 1 **Convert to a Smaller Unit**	Example 2 **Convert to a Larger Unit**
5 L = _____ mL	300 mL = _____ L
Multiply because we will need more of the smaller units.	Divide because we will need fewer of the larger units.
Convert liters to milliliters.	**Convert milliliters to liters.**
Multiply by 1,000 because 1 L = 1,000 mL.	Divide by 1,000 because 1,000 mL = 1 L.
5 L = <u>5,000</u> mL (1,000 × 5 = 5,000)	300 mL = <u>0.3</u> L (300 ÷ 1,000 = 0.3)

Complete.

1. 49 L = _____ mL

2. 5.68 kL = _____ L

3. 508 mL = _____ L

4. 8.6 L = _____ cL

5. 483 cL = _____ L

6. 227 mL = _____ L

7. 2.9 L = _____ mL

8. 4,873 L = _____ kL

9. 1,992 mL = _____ L

10. 43 L = _____ kL

11. 41 kL = _____ L

12. 58 cL = _____ L

Multistep Problem Solving

Solve. Check that your answer is reasonable.

Show your work.

13 Morgan's juice glass holds 225 milliliters. If she uses the glass to drink 8 glasses of water every day, how many liters of water does Morgan drink during a week?

14 Erin's water bottle holds 665 milliliters. Dylan is carrying two water bottles. Each one holds 0.35 liters. Who is carrying more water? How much more?

15 Sarita is selling lemonade in 300-milliliter bottles. She made two batches of lemonade. Each batch made 4.6 liters of lemonade. How much lemonade will she have left over after filling her bottles?

16 Kelly is using a bucket to fill up a barrel with water from a well. The barrel holds 25.5 liters. The bucket holds 800 milliliters. The barrel already has 5.2 liters of water in it. What is the least number of buckets needed to fill the barrel?

17 Tammy is making 5 batches of fruit drink for soccer practice. The recipe for one batch uses 1 liter of orange juice, 550 milliliters of lemon juice, 2.6 liters of soda water, and two 750 milliliter bottles of apple cider. How many liters of fruit drink will she make?

✓ **Check Understanding**

Draw a diagram that shows how to convert 20 milliliters to centiliters.

© Houghton Mifflin Harcourt Publishing Company

Metric Units of Liquid Volume

Convert Units of Mass

A gram is the basic unit of metric mass. This chart shows the relationship between grams and other metric units of mass.

Metric Units of Mass	
1 dekagram (dag) = 10 grams	1 gram = 0.1 dekagram
1 hectogram (hg) = 100 grams	1 gram = 0.01 hectogram
1 kilogram (kg) = 1,000 grams	1 gram = 0.001 kilogram
1 gram = 10 decigrams (dg)	0.1 gram = 1 decigram
1 gram = 100 centigrams (cg)	0.01 gram = 1 centigram
1 gram = 1,000 milligrams (mg)	0.001 gram = 1 milligram
Example 1 Convert to a Smaller Unit 5 kg = _____ g Multiply because we will need more of the smaller units. **Convert kilograms to grams.** Multiply by 1,000 because 1 kg = 1,000 g. 5 kg = __5,000__ g (1000 × 5 = 5,000)	**Example 2 Convert to a Larger Unit** 700 mg = _____ g Divide because we will need fewer of the larger units. **Convert milligrams to grams.** Divide by 1,000 because 1,000 mg = 1 g. 700 mg = __0.7__ g (700 ÷ 1,000 = 0.7)

Complete.

1 0.003 g = _____ mg

2 3.05 kg = _____ g

3 25 mg = _____ g

4 5.7 g = _____ mg

5 294 mg = 0.294 _____

6 0.032 g = 32 _____

7 13.7 g = _____ mg

8 2,441 g = _____ kg

9 8,240 mg = _____ g

10 75 g = 0.075 _____

11 0.43 kg = _____ g

12 721 mg = _____ g

Multistep Problem Solving

Solve. Check that your answer is reasonable.   *Show your work.*

13 Hiro has 5 kilograms of potatoes and 2 kilograms of onions. He plans to use 3.25 kilograms of potatoes and 550 grams of onions for a recipe. How many total kilograms of the produce will not be used?

_____

14 A U.S. nickel has a mass of 5.00 grams. A U.S. penny has a mass of 2.50 grams. What is the mass in kilograms of the coins in a bag containing 186 nickels and 72 pennies?

_____

15 Jerry is making trail mix for his camping trip. He has 200 grams of peanuts, 350 grams of raisins, and 735 grams of pretzels. He wants to make 2 kilograms of trail mix. How many more grams of ingredients does he need to add to the mix?

_____

16 Garner is helping his mom carry in the groceries. She is carrying a bag that has a mass of 1.33 kilograms. Garner is carrying two bags. One has a mass of 580 grams and the other a mass of 790 grams. Who is carrying more and by how much?

_____

17 Mr. Frank has 1.03 kilograms of fertilizer for the plants in his nursery. He wants every plant to get 95 mg of fertilizer 4 times each year. What is the number of plants he could fertilize with that amount? How much fertilizer will he have left over?

_____

✔ Check Understanding

Explain how you would decide if a mass given in milligrams is more or less than a mass given in kilograms.

Metric Units of Mass

Fractions and Liquid Volume

In the United States we use customary units to measure.

Customary Units of Liquid Volume						
1 gallon (gal)	=	4 quarts	=	8 pints	=	16 cups (c)
$\frac{1}{4}$ gallon	=	1 quart (qt)	=	2 pints	=	4 cups
$\frac{1}{8}$ gallon	=	$\frac{1}{2}$ quart	=	1 pint (pt)	=	2 cups

Answer with a fraction in simplest form.

1 What fraction of 1 gallon is 3 quarts?

_____

2 What fraction of 1 quart is 1 pint?

_____

3 What fraction of 1 quart is 1 cup?

_____

4 What fraction of 1 gallon is 3 pints?

_____

Example 1 **Convert to a Smaller Unit**	Example 2 **Convert to a Larger Unit**
12 qt = _____ cups	104 pt = _____ gal
Multiply because we will need more of the smaller units.	Divide because we will need fewer of the larger units.
Convert quarts to cups.	**Convert pints to gallons.**
Multiply by 4 because 1 qt = 4 cups.	Divide by 8 because 8 pt = 1 gal.
12 qt = __48__ cups (4 × 12 = 48)	104 pt = __13__ gal (104 ÷ 8 = 13)

Complete.

5 20 cups = _____ qt

6 _____ pt = 2 gal

7 15 qt = _____ cups

8 3 cups = _____ pt

9 _____ gal = 48 qt

10 144 cups = _____ gal

11 _____ pt = $2\frac{1}{2}$ qt

12 23 pt = _____ cups

13 _____ qt = $1\frac{1}{2}$ gal

Solve Multistep Problems

Solve. Check that your answer is reasonable. When possible, express your answer as a whole or mixed number.

Show your work.

14 A muffin recipe requires $2\frac{3}{4}$ cups of milk. How many quarts of milk do you need to make double the number of muffins?

_____

15 A recipe requires $\frac{3}{4}$ cup of water. Farha has a measuring cup that is marked only in ounces, but she knows that 8 ounces is equivalent to 1 cup. How many ounces of water will she add to the mixture? Explain.

_____

_____

16 A serving size for sports drink is $\frac{1}{2}$ cup. Liam needs to make 72 servings. He will use 8 pints of sports drink concentrate. The rest is water. How many pints of water does he need to make the sports drink?

_____

17 Melanie and Brad each drink 10 cups of water every day. Lara drinks 3 quarts of water every day. How many gallons of water do the three of them drink altogether each week?

_____

18 Angela and Ryou are painting a room. Angela has $2\frac{1}{2}$ gallons of blue paint and Ryou has half as much white paint. It will take $2\frac{3}{4}$ quarts to cover each wall. If each wall is painted only one color, how many walls will be blue and how many will be white? How much paint will be left over?

_____

_____

✓ **Check Understanding**

Explain why you should divide to convert quarts to gallons.

Fractions and Weight

VOCABULARY
ton (T)

Customary units of weight include ounces, pounds, and **tons**.

ounce (oz)	pound (lb)	ton (T)
1 lb = 16 oz	1 lb	1 T = 2,000 lb

1 The table below shows how to use fractions to compare ounces to pounds. Complete the table by writing each fraction in simplest form.

Ounces (oz)	1	2	4	8	12
Pounds (lb)	$\frac{1}{16}$	$\frac{1}{8}$			

Example 1 **Convert to a Smaller Unit**	Example 2 **Convert to a Larger Unit**
4 T = _____ lb	144 oz = _____ lb
Multiply because we will need more of the smaller units.	Divide because we will need fewer of the larger units.
Convert tons to pounds.	**Convert ounces to pounds.**
Multiply by 2,000 because 1 T = 2,000 lb.	Divide by 16 because 16 oz = 1 lb.
4 T = 8,000 lb (2000 × 4 = 8,000)	144 oz = __9__ lb (144 ÷ 16 = 9)

Complete.

2 64 oz = _____ lb

3 _____ T = 10,000 lb

4 11 T = _____ lb

5 16 lb = _____ oz

6 _____ T = 14,000 lb

7 160 oz = _____ lb

8 _____ oz = $5\frac{1}{4}$ lb

9 848 oz = _____ lb

10 _____ lb = 720 oz

Solve Multistep Problems

Solve. Check that your answer is reasonable.

11 A $\frac{1}{4}$-lb package of sunflower seeds costs 79¢. An 8-oz package costs $1.59. Which package represents the lower cost per oz?

_____

12 Mel is measuring 132 oz of rice into one-pound containers. How many one-pound containers will she need to hold all of the rice? How many more ounces of rice will she need to buy if she needs a total of 10 pounds of rice?

_____

_____

13 A casserole recipe calls for 4 ounces of cheese. Adrian wants to use $\frac{1}{2}$ of the amount of cheese in his casseroles. How many pounds of cheese does he need to make 28 casseroles with his revised recipe? Write your answer as a mixed number.

_____

14 The four elephants at the Sunnypark Zoo each eat 150 pounds of food a day. How many tons of food do the four elephants eat during the month of April?

_____

15 A cargo truck is carrying three identical boxes. The weight of each box is $2\frac{1}{2}$ tons. What is the total weight of the boxes in pounds? Use mental math if you can.

_____

✓**Check Understanding**

Choose one of the problems above and explain how you solved it.

Customary Units of Weight

Line Plots with Fractional Units

VOCABULARY
frequency table
line plot

Soil samples were taken for 10 days for a biology project. The **frequency table** below shows the number of times the various weights for the samples occurred. You can organize data on a **line plot** to make the data easier to analyze.

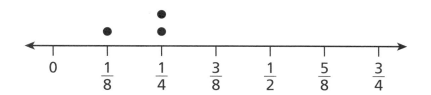

Weight of Samples (lb)	Number of Samples
$\frac{1}{8}$	1
$\frac{1}{4}$	2
$\frac{3}{8}$	3
$\frac{1}{2}$	2
$\frac{5}{8}$	2

1 The line plot has been filled in for sample weights of $\frac{1}{8}$ and $\frac{1}{4}$ lb. Complete the rest of the line plot.

2 Based on these samples, which sample weight is least likely to occur?

3 Based on these samples, which sample weight is most likely to occur?

4 What is the total weight of the samples weighing $\frac{3}{8}$ lb?

5 If the total weight of the samples were redistributed evenly among the 10 samples, what would each sample weigh? Explain how you found your answer.

Line Plots with Fractional Units (continued)

6 For 10 days, Mario measured the amount of food that his cat Toby ate each day. The amounts he recorded are shown in the table at the right. Graph the results on the line plot.

Amounts Toby Ate Each Day for 10 Days	
$\frac{1}{4}$ c	||
$\frac{3}{8}$ c	|
$\frac{1}{2}$ c	|||
$\frac{5}{8}$ c	|||
$\frac{3}{4}$ c	|

a. What is the total amount of food Toby ate over the 10 days? Explain how you got your answer.

_____

_____

b. What amount of food would Toby get each day if the total for 10 days

were distributed evenly each day? _____

7 Lilly bought a bag of beads of mixed sizes. She made the frequency table below showing the number of beads of each size. Make a line plot using her data. Write a question that can be solved using the line plot.

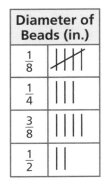

Diameter of Beads (in.)	
$\frac{1}{8}$	|||||
$\frac{1}{4}$	|||
$\frac{3}{8}$	||||
$\frac{1}{2}$	||

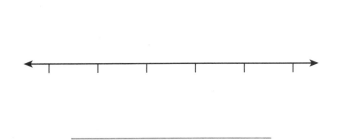

_____

_____

_____

_____

_____

Check Understanding

If all the beads in Problem 7 were strung together, how long would the string of beads be?

Read and Make Line Plots

Complete.

1 12 cups = _____ qt

2 240 g = _____ kg

Solve.

3 The 5 horses on Miranda's farm each eat 20 pounds of feed per day. How many tons of feed do the horses eat in 30 days?

4 Dante's mom made 2 liters of cocoa. Dante and his 5 friends each drank a serving of cocoa. If each serving is 325 milliliters, how much cocoa is left?

5 Emily bags and weighs dog treats in the bulk section of a pet store. She records the weights of the bags in the table. Circle the line plot that displays the data in the table.

Weight of Dog Treats (lb)						
$\frac{1}{2}$	$\frac{5}{8}$	$\frac{3}{4}$	$\frac{7}{8}$	1	$1\frac{1}{8}$	$1\frac{1}{4}$
卌		|||			||	|||

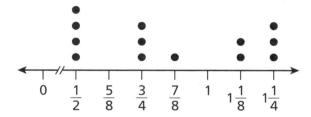

Weights of Dog Treats (lb)

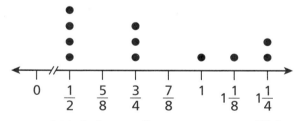

Weights of Dog Treats (lb)

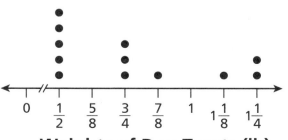

Weights of Dog Treats (lb)

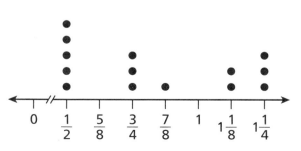

Weights of Dog Treats (lb)

Fluency Check 13

Name ______________________ Date ______________

PATH to FLUENCY

Multiply.

1. 80×4

2. 38×4

3. 700×5

4. 409×6

5. 510×9

6. 761×6

7. 821×7

8. $5{,}000 \times 8$

9. $2{,}090 \times 5$

10. $6{,}704 \times 3$

11. $3{,}976 \times 9$

12. 20×70

13. 37×60

14. 58×83

15. 61×49

Reasoning About Quadrilaterals

In Exercises 1–6, write *true* or *false*. If the statement is false, sketch a counterexample.

1 All quadrilaterals have at least one pair of parallel sides.

2 All squares have at least 1 pair of perpendicular sides.

3 A rhombus must have an acute angle.

4 All rectangles have opposite sides that are the same length.

5 All squares have opposite sides that are parallel.

6 A quadrilateral with a right angle must be a rectangle.

Sketch a shape that fits the description if possible.

7 a parallelogram with exactly two right angles

8 a trapezoid with one line of symmetry

9 a rectangle with adjacent sides that are the same length

10 a square that is not a rhombus

Classify Quadrilaterals

A **quadrilateral** is a closed shape with four straight sides. The diagram below shows how the categories of quadrilaterals are related.

VOCABULARY
quadrilateral
parallelogram
trapezoid
rectangle
rhombus
square

⓫ List the letters of the shapes from Quadrilaterals A–T on page 388A that belong in each category. (Many shapes belong to more than one category.) Then complete the statements.

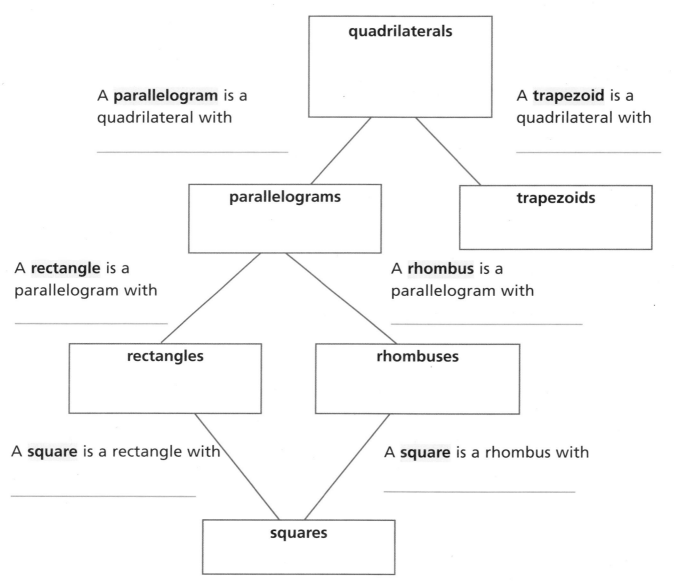

A **parallelogram** is a quadrilateral with

_____

A **trapezoid** is a quadrilateral with

_____

A **rectangle** is a parallelogram with

_____

A **rhombus** is a parallelogram with

_____

A **square** is a rectangle with

_____

A **square** is a rhombus with

_____

✔ **Check Understanding**

Explain why all squares are rhombuses but not all rhombuses are squares.

Attributes of Quadrilaterals

Name _____

Quadrilateral Cards

quadrilateral	quadrilateral	quadrilateral	quadrilateral
A	B	C	D
quadrilateral	quadrilateral	quadrilateral	quadrilateral
E	F	G	H
quadrilateral	quadrilateral	quadrilateral	quadrilateral
I	J	K	L
quadrilateral	quadrilateral	quadrilateral	quadrilateral
M	N	O	P
quadrilateral	quadrilateral	quadrilateral	quadrilateral
Q	R	S	T

Attributes of Quadrilaterals

Reasoning About Triangles

In Exercises 1–6, write *true* or *false*. If the statement is false, sketch a counterexample.

1 All isosceles triangles are also equilateral.

2 A scalene triangle cannot have a line of symmetry.

3 All right triangles have two acute angles.

4 Any triangle with an obtuse angle must be scalene.

5 All equilateral triangles are acute.

6 A scalene triangle cannot have a right angle.

Sketch a shape that fits the description if possible.

7 an isosceles triangle with a right angle

8 a triangle with two right angles

9 a triangle with more than one line of symmetry

10 an isosceles triangle without a line of symmetry

Classify Triangles

Write the letters of the shapes from Triangles A–L from page 390A in the correct region of each diagram.

VOCABULARY
acute triangle
obtuse triangle
right triangle
equilateral triangle
isosceles triangle
scalene triangle

11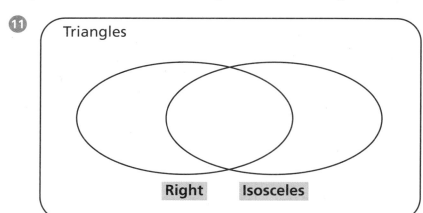

Triangles

Right   Isosceles

12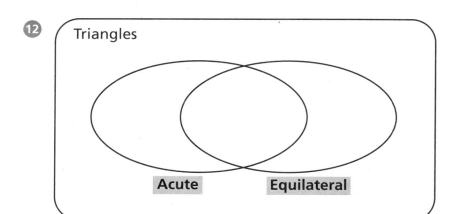

Triangles

Acute   Equilateral

13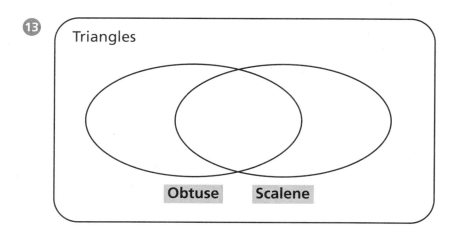

Triangles

Obtuse   Scalene

✓ **Check Understanding**
Draw a triangle that is both obtuse and isosceles.

Attributes of Triangles

Name _____

Triangle Cards

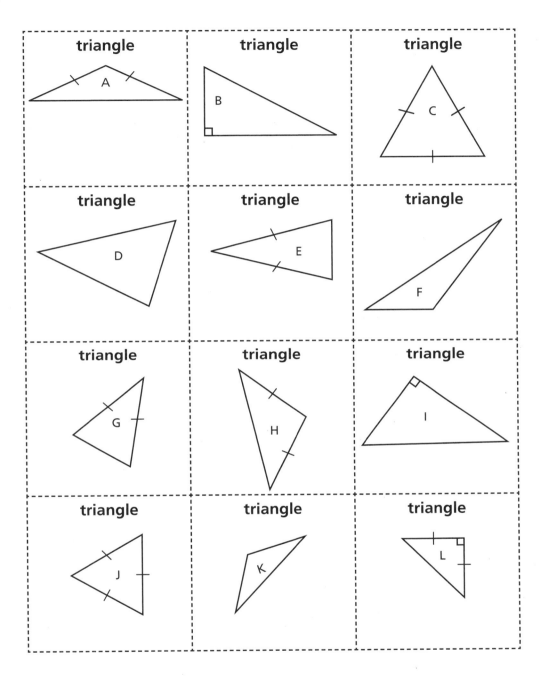

Attributes of Triangles **390A**

Attributes of Triangles

Two-Dimensional Shapes

VOCABULARY
open shape
closed shape
polygon
concave polygon
convex polygon

Two-dimensional shapes can be made up of line segments or curves or both.

Two-dimensional shapes can be **open shapes** or **closed shapes**.

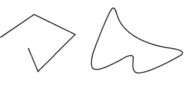

A **polygon** is a closed two-dimensional shape made from line segments that don't cross each other.

polygons   **not polygons**

A polygon is a **concave polygon** if you can connect two points inside the polygon with a line segment that passes outside the polygon. A **convex polygon** has no such line segment. All the inside angles of a convex polygon are less than 180°.

concave   convex

Tell whether each figure is a polygon. If it is not a polygon, explain why it does not fit the definition.

1

_____
_____

2

_____
_____

3

_____
_____

4

_____
_____

5

_____
_____

6

_____
_____

Names of Polygons

VOCABULARY
regular polygon

Polygons are named by the number of sides they have.
Here are some polygons with their names.

triangle	quadrilateral	pentagon	hexagon	octagon
3 sides	4 sides	5 sides	6 sides	8 sides

Polygons in which all sides are congruent *and* all angles are
congruent are called **regular polygons**. The octagon above
is a regular octagon.

Name the polygon. Then circle the terms that describe it.

  _____

regular	not regular
concave	convex

  _____

regular	not regular
concave	convex

  _____

regular	not regular
concave	convex

  _____

regular	not regular
concave	convex

Write *true* or *false*.

11 A square is a regular quadrilateral. _____

12 It is possible to draw a concave triangle. _____

 Check Understanding

Look at the figure on the right and describe it
using as many geometry terms as possible.

Attributes of Two-Dimensional Shapes

Name _____

Two-Dimensional Shape Cards

2-D shape	2-D shape	2-D shape	2-D shape
A	B	C	D
2-D shape	2-D shape	2-D shape	2-D shape
E	F	G	H
2-D shape	2-D shape	2-D shape	2-D shape
I	J	K	L
2-D shape	2-D shape	2-D shape	2-D shape
M	N	O	P

Attributes of Two-Dimensional Shapes **392A**

Attributes of Two-Dimensional Shapes

Attribute Cards

concave polygon	convex polygon	straight sides	curved
open shape	closed shape	polygon	regular polygon
at least one pair of parallel sides	at least one pair of perpendicular sides	line of symmetry	at least two congruent sides
acute angle	right angle	obtuse angle	angle greater than 180°

Attributes of Two-Dimensional Shapes

Name _____

Math and Aquariums

A goldfish bowl is a small aquarium. Other aquariums, like those found in museums, can be enormous and have computer monitored and controlled life-support systems.

Many home aquariums are made of glass or acrylic, and are shaped like rectangular prisms. A sketch of Naomi's home aquarium is shown at the right.

Use the sketch to solve Problems 1 and 2.

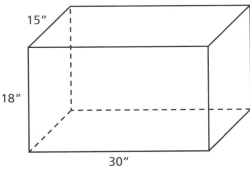

15"
18"
30"

1 Which faces of Naomi's aquarium—the top and bottom, the sides, or the front and back—have the greatest perimeter?

_____

2 Use a formula and find the area of each of the following faces.

top and bottom _____

left side and right side _____

front and back _____

3 Use a formula and find the volume of the aquarium.

_____

Math and Aquariums (continued)

Residents of salt water aquariums often include colorful fish. Some salt water aquariums also include living plants, rocks, and corals.

Use the sketch of Naomi's aquarium shown below to solve Problems 4–6.

4 Suppose three inches of sand were placed in the bottom of the aquarium. Calculate the remaining volume of the aquarium.

_____

5 Naomi would like to attach rubber edging along the top edges, and along the bottom edges, of her aquarium. Use a formula to determine the minimum length of edging Naomi would need.

_____

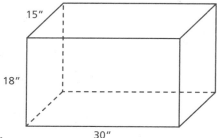

6 Suppose Naomi would like to place a flat sheet of acrylic under her aquarium, with the sheet extending 1-inch beyond the edges of her aquarium in all directions. What are the dimensions of acrylic sheet she should purchase?

_____

Solve.

7 Explain how you could change your answers to Problem 2 to square feet, and your answer to Problem 3 to cubic feet.

_____

_____

_____

_____

1 Explain why this trapezoid is a quadrilateral but not a parallelogram.

_____

_____

_____

2 Circle the figure that is a convex pentagon with one pair of parallel sides.

   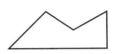

3 Rae classifies a rectangle as a quadrilateral and a parallelogram. Explain why Rae is or is not correct.

_____

_____

_____

_____

Write all the names from the box that describe the polygon.

quadrilateral	parallelogram	acute triangle	equilateral triangle
rectangle	rhombus	obtuse triangle	isosceles triangle
square	trapezoid	right triangle	scalene triangle

4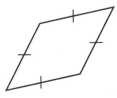

_____

5

_____

Name _____ **Date** _____

Multiply.

1 50
  × 6

2 76
  × 6

3 400
  × 9

4 560
  × 2

5 308
  × 5

6 824
  × 4

7 679
  × 7

8 7,000
  × 8

9 6,600
  × 3

10 5,309
  × 6

11 9,313
  × 4

12 80
  × 30

13 74
  × 50

14 82
  × 16

15 43
  × 69

Name _____

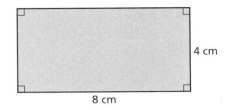

Area of a Right Triangle

1 What is the area of the rectangle shown here?

_____

2 Draw a diagonal line in the rectangle and make two triangles. What is the area of each triangle? Why do you think so?

16 cm² — The rectangle has bendivided

4 cm

8 cm

$$\begin{array}{r} 0 \\ 15 \\ \times\ 20 \\ \hline 0 \end{array}$$

A triangle with a right angle (square corner) is called a right triangle. The area of any right triangle is half the area of a rectangle with the same base and height.

What is the area of each shaded right triangle shown below?

3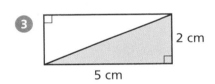

2 cm

5 cm

5 cm²

4 64 ½ A=

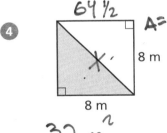

8 m

8 m

32 m²

5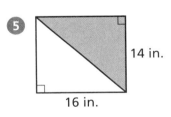

14 in.

16 in.

_____

Find the area of each triangle. Mark the right angle with a small box.

6

12 in.

12 in.

72 in.

7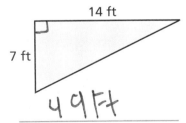

14 ft

7 ft

49 ft

8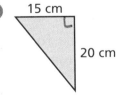

15 cm

20 cm

_____

9 Let b = the length of the base and h = the height. Write a formula for finding the area of any right triangle.

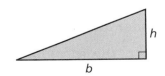

h

b

_____

Congruent

Find the Area

Find the area of each rectangle. Then find the area of each shaded triangle.

10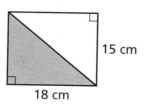
15 cm
18 cm

11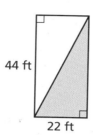
44 ft
22 ft

12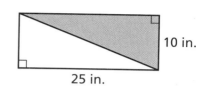
10 in.
25 in.

Area of rectangle:

_____

Area of triangle:

_____

Area of rectangle:

_____

Area of triangle:

_____

Area of rectangle:

_____

Area of triangle:

_____

Solve.

13 Lotte divided her rectangular flower garden into two sections for pink and yellow roses. What is the area of each section? _____

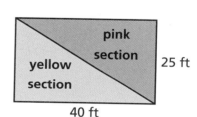
pink section
yellow section
25 ft
40 ft

14 The banner for the Mountaineers Club is shown.

a. What area of the banner is colored green?

_____

b. What area of the banner is colored blue?

_____

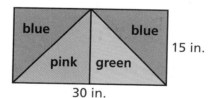
blue   blue
pink   green
15 in.
30 in.

15 Write a formula for finding the area of the shaded right triangle with sides s.

_____

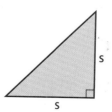
s
s

✓ Check Understanding

Explain why the formula $A = \frac{1}{2} \cdot b \cdot h$ can be used to find the area of any right triangle.

Name _____

Find the Area of a Parallelogram

Rectangle A has base **b** and height **h**.

Rectangle A

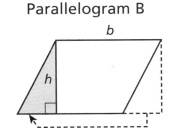

7 How can you express the area of Rectangle A
in terms of *b* and *h*? Write a formula.

_____

The shaded triangle from above is now cut out and
attached to the left side of Rectangle A to form
Parallelogram B.

Parallelogram B

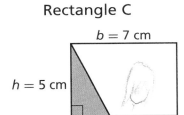

8 How do the areas of the two figures
compare? Explain.

_____

_____

_____

Rectangle C has base of 7 cm and height of 5 cm.

Rectangle C

$b = 7$ cm

$h = 5$ cm

9 What is the area of Rectangle C?

_____

10 What is the area of Parallelogram D? Explain.

Parallelogram D

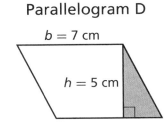

$b = 7$ cm

$h = 5$ cm

_____

_____

_____

11 What formula can you write to find the area of a
parallelogram if you know the value of *b* and *h*? Explain.

_____

_____

Name _____

Experiment with Parallelograms

The **height of a parallelogram** is a line segment **perpendicular** to the **base of the parallelogram**.

VOCABULARY
height of a parallelogram
base of a parallelogram
perpendicular

Cut out each pair of parallelograms below and then cut along the dotted line that shows each height. Switch the pieces. Put the slanted ends together.

What figure do you form?

_____

Do you think it will always happen? Why or why not?

_____

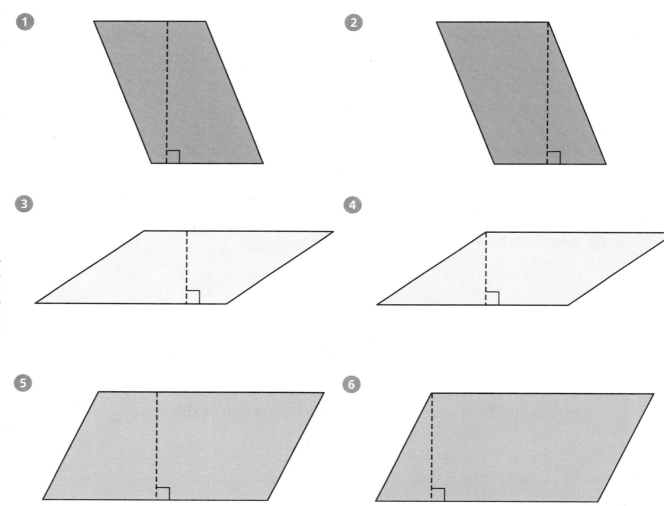

Area of a Parallelogram **399A**

Area of a Parallelogram

bottom = base

Area and Perimeter of Parallelograms

height = dots

Find the area and perimeter of each parallelogram. *Pre = add all sides*

12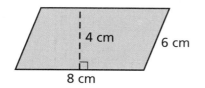

A = _____

P = _____

13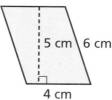

A = _____

P = _____

14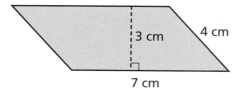

A = _____

P = _____

15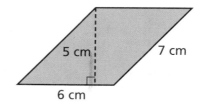

A = _____

P = _____

16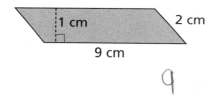

9

A = _____

P = _____

17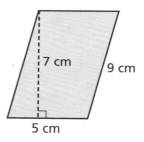

A = _____

P = _____

Solve.

18 The base of this parallelogram is 24 cm and its area
is 456 sq cm. What is the height of the parallelogram?

_____

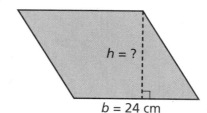

✓ **Check Understanding**

Explain how you know which measurement in
Exercise 16 is the *height* of the parallelogram.

Area of a Parallelogram

Name _____

Calculate the Area of a Triangle

The parallelogram shown has base *b* and height *h*.

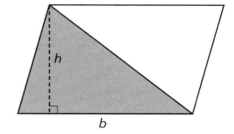

1 What is the area of the parallelogram in terms of *b* and *h*?

_____

2 How does the area of the shaded triangle compare to the area of the unshaded triangle?

_____

_____

_____

3 How does the area of the shaded triangle compare to the area of the parallelogram?

_____

4 Write a formula for the area of the shaded triangle in terms of *b* and *h*.

_____

5 Write a formula for the area of any triangle. What measurements do you need to know to find the area of any triangle?

_____

Find the area of each triangle.

6

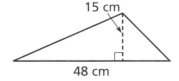

15 cm

48 cm

7

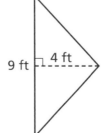

9 ft   4 ft

8

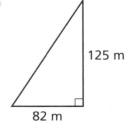

125 m

82 m

_____   _____   _____

Experiment with Triangles

The acute triangles below are exactly the same. Cut them out
and place sides *a* together. What shape do you form?
Do the same with sides *b* and *c*.

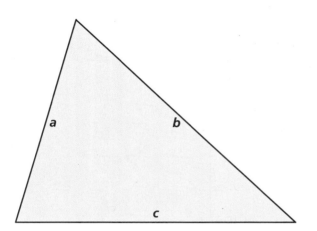 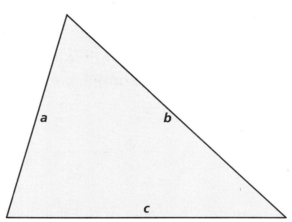

The obtuse triangles below are exactly the same. Cut them out
and place sides *x* together. What shape do you form?
Do the same with sides *y* and *z*.

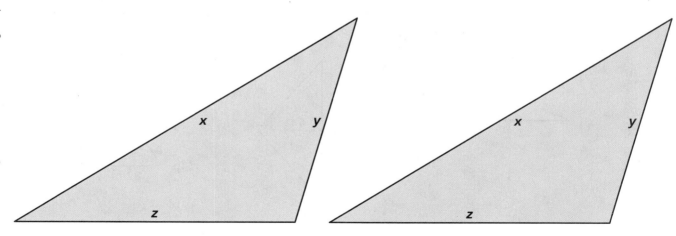

Area of Any Triangle

Find the Area of Triangles

Find the area of each triangle below.
Identify each triangle as right, acute, or obtuse.

9

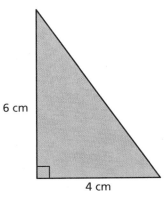

6 cm

4 cm

10

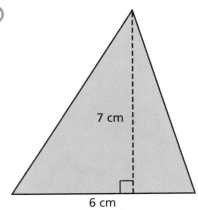

7 cm

6 cm

11

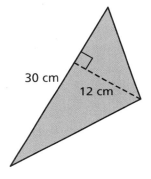

30 cm

12 cm

12

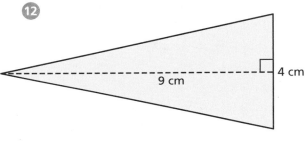

9 cm

4 cm

13.

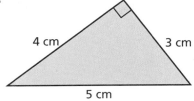

4 cm

3 cm

5 cm

14

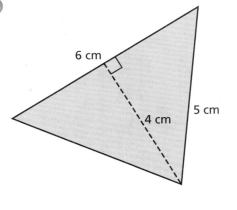

6 cm

5 cm

4 cm

Area of Any Triangle

The Base and Height of a Triangle

Any side of a triangle can be the **base of the triangle**.
For each base, the **height** is a line segment or the measure
of a line segment that begins at the **vertex** opposite the base
and forms a right angle with the base.

VOCABULARY
base of a triangle
height of a triangle
vertex

The base is side *AB*.
The height is *CD*.

The base is side *BC*.
The height is *AE*.

The base is side *AC*.
The height is *BF*.

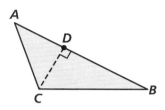 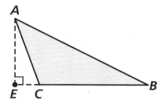 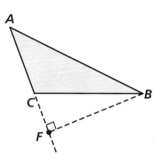

15 How are the three heights for Triangle *ABC* the same?

_____

_____

16 How are the three heights for Triangle *ABC* different?

_____

_____

_____

17 Draw the height from vertex *N*.

18 Draw the height from vertex *M*.

19 Draw the height from vertex *L*.

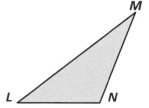 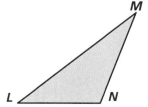 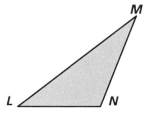

The base is side ____.

The base is side ____.

The base is side ____.

Select Appropriate Measurements

Find the area of each triangle.

20
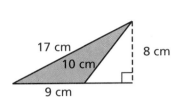

21
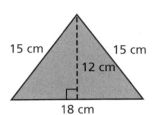

22
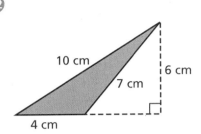

_____   _____   _____

Solve Real World Problems

Solve.

23 Jared wants to carpet this triangular part of his basement floor. How much carpet will he use?

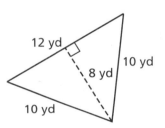

_____

24 Rona drew this pattern for a sail for a miniature sailboat. How much cloth will she need to make four sails using this pattern?

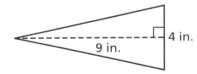

_____

25 Babette wants to paint this triangular portion of her bedroom wall purple. What is the area of the space she needs to paint?

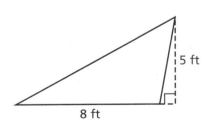

_____

✓ **Check Understanding**
Explain how finding the area of a triangle is related to finding the area of a parallelogram.

Area of Any Triangle

VOCABULARY
dimensions

Select Appropriate Measurements

Discuss the **dimensions** you need to find the perimeter of a triangle.

Figure A	Figure B	Figure C

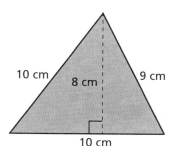
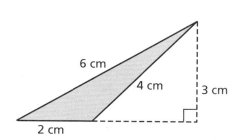
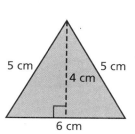

Find the perimeter of each triangle.

1 Figure A _____

2 Figure B _____

3 Figure C _____

**Discuss the dimensions you need to find the area of a triangle.
Find the area of each triangle.**

4 Figure A _____

5 Figure B _____

6 Figure C _____

Discuss the dimensions you need to find the perimeter and area of a parallelogram.

Figure D	Figure E	Figure F

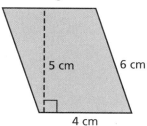
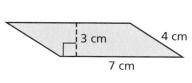
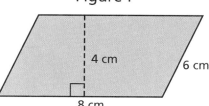

Find the perimeter of each parallelogram.

7 Figure D _____

8 Figure E _____

9 Figure F _____

Find the area of each parallelogram.

10 Figure D _____

11 Figure E _____

12 Figure F _____

Practice Finding Perimeter and Area

Find the perimeter and the area of each figure.

13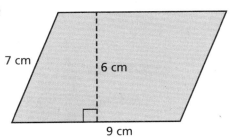

7 cm
6 cm
9 cm

P = _____

A = _____

14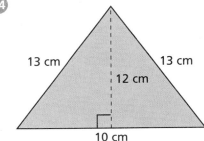

13 cm
13 cm
12 cm
10 cm

P = _____

A = _____

15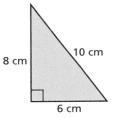

8 cm
10 cm
6 cm

P = _____

A = _____

16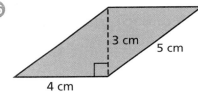

3 cm
5 cm
4 cm

P = _____

A = _____

17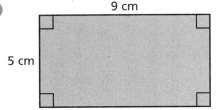

9 cm
5 cm

P = _____

A = _____

18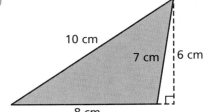

10 cm
7 cm
6 cm
8 cm

P = _____

A = _____

Area of Other Figures

Visualize Figures

⑲ Find the area of the triangle.

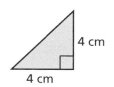

_____

⑳ Find the area of the rectangle.

_____

㉑ Find the area of the complex figure.

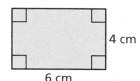

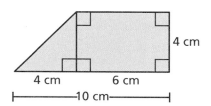

_____

Find Perimeter and Area of Complex Figures

Find the area and perimeter of these complex figures.

㉒

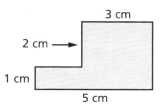

P = _____

A = _____

㉓

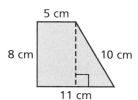

P = _____

A = _____

㉔

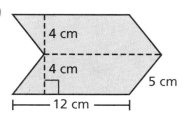

P = _____

A = _____

㉕

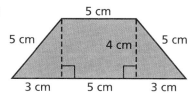

P = _____

A = _____

Solve.

㉖ Vadim needs to know the area of this pentagon, so he calls his friend Serena. Serena says she can figure out the area if Vadim will make just three measurements. Which three measurements does Vadim need to make?

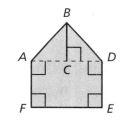

_____

© Houghton Mifflin Harcourt Publishing Company

Area of a Regular Pentagon

27 How many congruent isosceles triangles are inside the regular pentagon?

_____

28 Measure the base and the height of the isosceles triangle to the nearest centimeter.

_____

29 What is the area of the triangle?

_____

30 What is the area of the pentagon?

_____

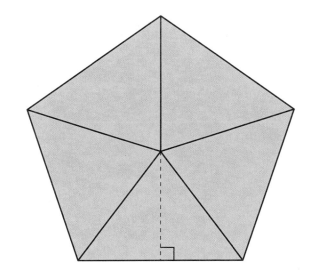

Area of a Regular Hexagon

31 Estimate the area of the regular hexagon by finding the area of the isosceles triangle. Show your work.

_____

_____

_____

_____

_____

_____

_____

_____

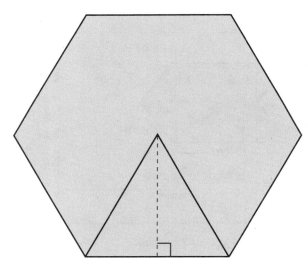

✓ **Check Understanding**
Find the area of this figure.

_____

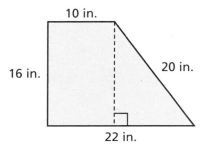

10 in.

16 in.   20 in.

22 in.

Find the area of each triangle.

1

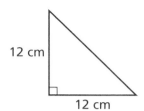

12 cm

12 cm

_____

2

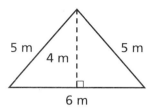

5 m   4 m   5 m

6 m

_____

3 Find the area and perimeter of the figure.

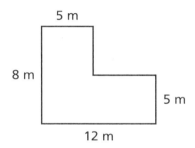

5 m

8 m

5 m

12 m

_____

4 The area of a parallelogram is 84 square feet. The height is 6 feet. What is the length of the base?

_____

5 What is the area of the pentagon?

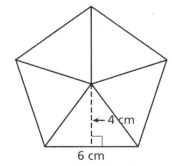

← 4 cm

6 cm

_____

Name   Date

PATH to
FLUENCY

Multiply.

1) 50
   × 8

2) 76
   × 9

3) 600
   ×   9

4) 560
   ×   6

5) 412
   ×   5

6) 492
   ×   4

7) 679
   ×   8

8) 4,000
   ×   8

9) 6,600
   ×   7

10) 7,054
   ×   6

11) 9,313
   ×   3

12) 90
   ×30

13) 74
   ×60

14) 29
   ×16

15) 73
   ×69

Some Three-Dimensional Figures

VOCABULARY
sphere
cylinder
cone

Figures such as circles, triangles, and squares are flat and two-dimensional. Solids such as **spheres, cylinders,** and **cones** are three-dimensional.

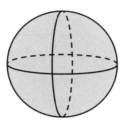

sphere

cylinder

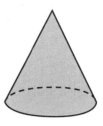

cone

1 Name two real world objects that have the shape of a sphere.

_____

_____

2 Name two real world objects that have the shape of a cylinder.

_____

_____

3 Name two real world objects that have the shape of a cone.

_____

_____

4 How are spheres, cylinders, and cones alike?

_____

_____

5 How are spheres, cylinders, and cones different?

_____

_____

_____

Cubes

VOCABULARY
cube
surface area
net

A **cube** is a three-dimensional figure made of congruent faces that are square.

6 How many faces does a cube have? _____

7 Name a real world object that is shaped like a cube.

_____

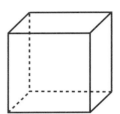

8 Each edge of a cube measures 3 cm. What is the total area of all of the faces? _____

9 Why is the total area of its faces called the **surface area** of the cube?

_____

A **net** is a flat or plane figure that can be folded to form a three-dimensional figure. The net at the right can be folded to form a cube.

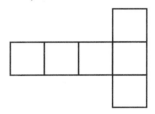

10 On a separate sheet of paper, draw several different nets for a cube.

Stacks of Cubes

How many cubes are in each stack?

11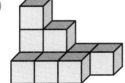

12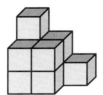

13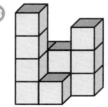

_____   _____   _____

✓ **Check Understanding**

How can you identify a three-dimensional figure as a cube?

Name _____

Make a Prism

A prism is a three-dimensional figure with two congruent (same size and shape) opposite faces called **bases**. Follow the steps below to make a **triangular prism**. The bases of your prism will be equilateral triangles whose sides measure 8 cm.

VOCABULARY
prism
base of a prism
triangular prism
congruent

1 Measure and cut out two congruent bases for your triangular prism.

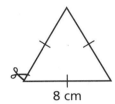

8 cm

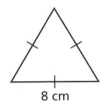

8 cm

2 Calculate the perimeter of one base.

$$8 + 8 + 8 = 24 \text{ cm}$$

$$3 \times 8 = 24 \text{ cm}$$

3 Cut a sheet of paper so that its length is the same as the perimeter of a base.

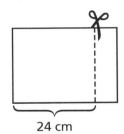

24 cm

4 Cut the paper to a height of your choice. This picture shows a height of 16 cm.

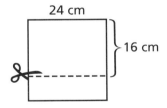

24 cm

16 cm

Hint: Don't cut your height too short.

5 Mark lines on the paper that divide the length into three equal parts.

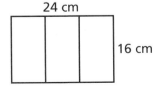

24 cm

16 cm

For a length of 24 cm, draw lines at 8 cm and 16 cm.

6 Fold along the lines and tape together the edges. Then tape the equilateral triangles to the top and bottom to make a prism.

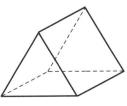

triangular prism

© Houghton Mifflin Harcourt Publishing Company

Prisms and Pyramids **413**

Name Prisms

VOCABULARY
pyramid

Name the shape of the base and use it to name the prism.

7

_____

_____

8

_____

_____

9

_____

_____

10

_____

_____

11

_____

_____

12

_____

_____

Name Pyramids

A **pyramid** is a three-dimensional figure with a polygon-shaped base and faces that meet at a point.

Name the shape of the base and use it to name the pyramid.

13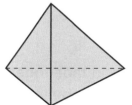

_____

14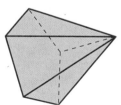

_____

15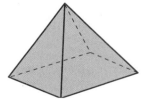

_____

16 How are pyramids and prisms alike?

_____

_____

Find Surface Area

Name each prism. Find the area of each face on the net.
Add the areas to find the surface area of each prism.

17

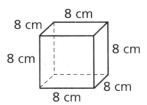

8 cm
8 cm
8 cm
8 cm
8 cm
8 cm
8 cm

8 cm
8 cm
8 cm
8 cm
8 cm
8 cm
8 cm
8 cm
8 cm

18

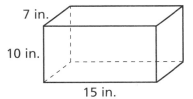

7 in.
10 in.
15 in.

7 in.
10 in.
7 in.
15 in.
7 in.
15 in.
7 in.

19

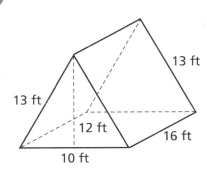

13 ft
13 ft
12 ft
10 ft

13 ft
13 ft
12 ft
10 ft
13 ft
13 ft
16 ft

13 ft
12 ft
13 ft

20 How can you find the surface area of any prism?

_____

_____

Match Nets and Three-Dimensional Figures

Match each net to a three-dimensional figure.

 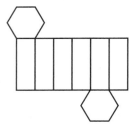

A

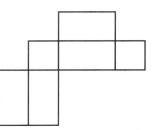

B

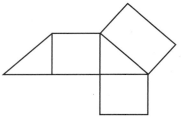

C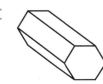

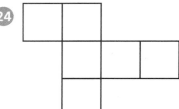

D

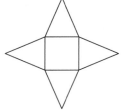

E

Check Understanding

How can you identify a prism or a pyramid just by looking at its net?

Prisms and Pyramids

Compare Three-Dimensional Figures

VOCABULARY
vertices

Name each three-dimensional figure.

1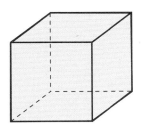

2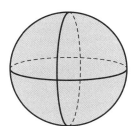

3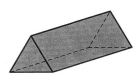

_____

_____

_____

4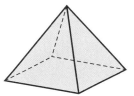

5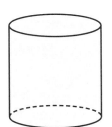

6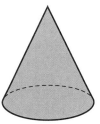

_____

_____

_____

Discuss Faces, Edges, and Vertices

Write the number of faces, edges, and vertices for each figure.

7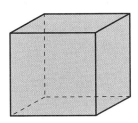

8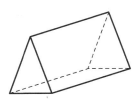

9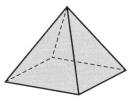

_____

_____

_____

_____

_____

_____

_____

_____

_____

Faces, Edges, and Vertices of Prisms

A decagon has 10 sides. You can use patterns to predict the number of faces, edges, and vertices of a prism with a decagon as a base.

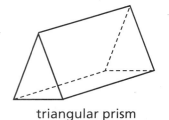

triangular prism

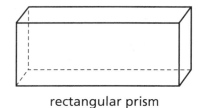

rectangular prism

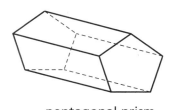

pentagonal prism

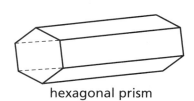

hexagonal prism

10 Use the prisms above to complete the next three rows of the chart.

Type of Prism	Number of Sides on Base	Number of Faces	Number of Edges	Number of Vertices
Triangular	3	5	9	6
Rectangular				
Pentagonal				
Hexagonal				
Decagonal				

11 What rule could you use to find the number of faces?

_____

12 What rule could you use to find the number of edges?

_____

13 What rule could you use to find the number of vertices?

_____

14 Use your rules to complete the last row of the chart.

Compare Three-Dimensional Figures

Name _____

Faces, Edges, and Vertices of Pyramids

An octagon has eight sides. You can use patterns to predict the number of faces, edges, and vertices of a pyramid with an octagon as a base.

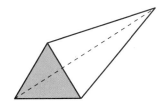

triangular pyramid

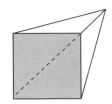

square pyramid

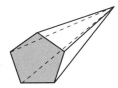

pentagonal pyramid

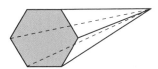

hexagonal pyramid

15 Use the pyramids above to complete the next three rows of the chart.

Type of Pyramid	Number of Sides on Base	Number of Faces	Number of Edges	Number of Vertices
Triangular	3	4	6	4
Rectangular				
Pentagonal				
Hexagonal				
Octagonal				

16 What rule could you use to find the number of faces?

_____

17 What rule could you use to find the number of edges?

_____

18 What rule could you use to find the number of vertices?

_____

19 Use your rules to complete the last row of the chart.

Compare Three-Dimensional Figures **419**

Compare Prisms and Pyramids

Use the figures below to complete the exercises.

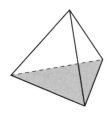

triangular pyramid

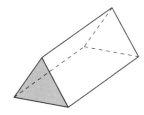

triangular prism

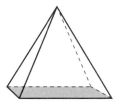

rectangular pyramid

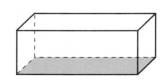

rectangular prism

20 How are pyramids and prisms named? Give an example.

_____

_____

21 How are pyramids and prisms alike?

_____

_____

22 How are pyramids and prisms different?

_____

_____

✔ **Check Understanding**

A three-dimensional figure has 1 base, 6 faces, 10 edges,

and 6 vertices. What is it? _____

A three-dimensional figure has 2 bases, 7 faces, 15 edges,

and 10 vertices. What is it? _____

Compare Three-Dimensional Figures

Name each solid.

1

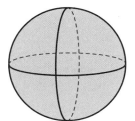

2

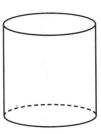

3

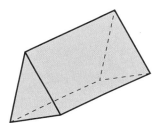

4

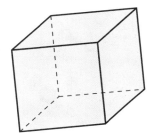

5 What solid figure does the net represent?

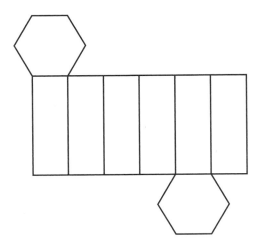

Name _____ **Date** _____

PATH to
FLUENCY

Multiply.

1   50
     × 9

2   89
     × 9

3   800
      × 9

4   560
     × 3

5   670
     × 5

6   282
     × 4

7   976
     × 8

8   4,000
      ×   4

9   6,600
      ×   6

10   4,507
       ×   6

11   9,313
       ×   7

12   20
      × 30

13   86
      × 60

14   83
      × 16

15   99
      × 69

1 Select the length that is equivalent to 0.14 meter. Mark all that apply.

Ⓐ 140 kilometers   Ⓒ 14 centimeters

Ⓑ 0.014 millimeter   Ⓓ 0.014 dekameter

2 Julian is making barbecue sauce that he will put into jars. He uses 15 cups of tomato sauce, 6 cups of white vinegar, $\frac{1}{2}$ cup of honey, and $\frac{1}{2}$ cup of maple syrup. How many quart jars can he fill? How many pint jars can he fill with any leftover sauce?

_____ quart jar(s) with _____ pint jar(s) leftover

3 Draw a net for a cube. Each square on the grid is 1 square unit. Calculate the surface area of the cube in square units.

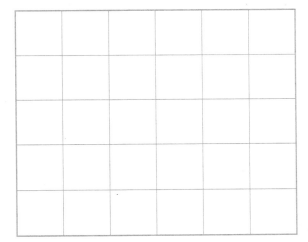

Surface area: _____

4 For Exercises 4a–4c, complete the conversion shown.

4a. 1,200 mL = _____ L

4b. _____ L = 6,000 mL

4c. _____ mg = 0.18 g

5 Find the area of the complex figure.

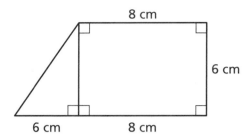

$A =$ _____

6 Identify the figure. Write the number of faces, edges, and vertices for the figure.

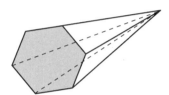

_____

7 Use a formula and calculate the volume of the figure.

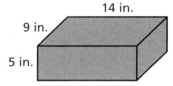

8 Write the missing dimensions of the figure. Then use a formula and calculate the volume of the figure.

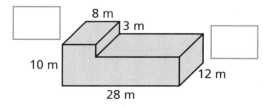

9 For Exercises 9a–9f, choose Yes or No to indicate whether the name applies to the polygon.

9a. quadrilateral   ○ Yes   ○ No

9b. rectangle   ○ Yes   ○ No

9c. square   ○ Yes   ○ No

9d. parallelogram   ○ Yes   ○ No

9e. rhombus   ○ Yes   ○ No

9f. trapezoid   ○ Yes   ○ No

10 Draw an isosceles triangle with a right angle.

11 A path is 0.75 meter wide. Mr. Kassel extends the width by placing blocks 20 centimeters wide on each side of the path. How many meters wide is the new path?

_____ meters

12 The east side of Mrs. Hammond's ranch is 475 meters longer than the west side. The west side is 2.6 kilometers long. How many kilometers long is the east side?

_____ kilometers

13 On a 1-mile walking tour of New York City, a group had to take a detour that was 100 yards shorter than half the distance of the tour. How many yards long is the detour?

_____ yards

14 Choose a number from the first column and a unit from the second column to make a measurement that is equivalent to 240 centigrams.

Number	Unit
○ 24	○ milligrams
○ 0.024	○ decigrams
○ 240	○ kilograms

15 A rectangular cedar chest measures 40 inches long by 22 inches wide by 20 inches high.

Part A

Find the volume of the chest.

Part B

A cushion is made to cover the top of the chest. Calculate the area of the chest that the cushion covers.

Part C

Explain any difference in the units for the volume and the area.

16 A door sign has a length of 5 inches and an area of 24 square inches. Use the numbers and symbols to write an equation that can be used to find the unknown width (w). Then solve.

$w =$ _____ inches

⑰ A souvenir postcard is $5\frac{1}{4}$ inches long and $3\frac{1}{2}$ inches wide. What is the area of the postcard?

⑱ Classify the figure using the terms in the boxes. Write the letter of the figure in the correct box. A figure may be classified using more than one term.

A   B   C 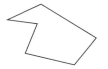 D   E F

Concave	Convex	Hexagon	Pentagon

⑲ Bakari builds a rectangular prism using unit cubes.

What is the volume of the prism? Explain your thinking.

⑳ For numbers 20a–20f, select True or False for each statement.

20a. A circle is a convex polygon. ○ True ○ False

20b. A rhombus can have only one right angle. ○ True ○ False

20c. All squares are rectangles. ○ True ○ False

20d. A regular octagon can be concave. ○ True ○ False

20e. A triangle can have at most one right angle. ○ True ○ False

20f. A regular triangle has three congruent angles. ○ True ○ False

21 Mika records the number of miles she walks each day.

Part A

Graph Mika's results on the line plot.

Distance (miles)	Days
$1\frac{1}{2}$	|||||
$1\frac{5}{8}$		
$1\frac{3}{4}$	||
2		
$2\frac{1}{8}$	|||
$2\frac{1}{4}$	||||

Miles Walked Each Day

Part B

How many days did she walk and what was her total distance? Explain your thinking.

22 Choose the term from the box to complete the statement.

22a. Every rectangle is also a | parallelogram / square / rhombus |.

22b. A trapezoid is also a | parallelogram / rhombus / quadrilateral |.

Planting Flowers

Cheryl used 1-inch thick wood to build a planter for some
flowers. The planter has 4 sides and a bottom,
but no top. The outside dimensions are 3 feet long,
$6\frac{1}{2}$ inches wide, and $6\frac{1}{2}$ inches high.

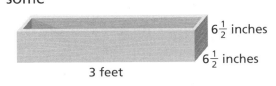

$6\frac{1}{2}$ inches

$6\frac{1}{2}$ inches

3 feet

1 What are the inside dimensions of the planter in inches?
What is the area of the inside bottom of the planter in
square inches? Explain how you found your answers.

_____

_____

_____

2 Cheryl wants to know the maximum volume of soil the
planter can hold. What is the volume of the soil the
planter can hold in cubic inches?

_____

3 Soil costs $0.02 per cubic inch. How many cubic inches of soil
does Cheryl need to fill the planter to $1\frac{1}{2}$ inches below the
top? How much will that much soil cost? Show your work.

_____

_____

4 Cheryl decides to build another planter. She will again use 1-inch
thick wood, but this planter will hold between 1,500 and 1,530
cubic inches of soil. What dimensions can she use if the length of
the planter will be less than or equal to 4 feet? What will be the
volume of soil?

_____

_____

_____

Cheryl also wants to build window box planters for 5 windows. To fit the windows, each box will be $1\frac{1}{4}$ yards long, 9 inches wide, and 8 inches high.

5 The boards for the bottom of the planters are 1 inch thick. The boards for the sides are $\frac{3}{4}$ inch thick. What are the inside dimensions of the finished planters in inches? Explain how you found your answer.

_____

_____

_____

6 Cheryl wants to fill the planters to 1 inch below the top with soil. She can purchase soil in bags containing 800 cubic inches; 1,000 cubic inches; and 1,500 cubic inches. What combination of bags can she purchase to fill the planters? How much soil will be left over? Show your work.

_____

_____

_____

7 Cheryl wants to paint the planters to match the color of the house. A gallon of paint covers 100 square feet. Will one-half gallon of paint be enough to paint the 3 visible sides as well as the bottom of each planter? Explain your answer. (Hint: 1 square foot = 144 square inches)

_____

_____

_____

_____

_____

Size of unit gets larger. →

Length

Kilometer (km) 1,000 m	Hectometer (hm) 100 m	Dekameter (dam) 10 m	METER (m) 1 m	Decimeter (dm) 0.1 m or $\frac{1}{10}$ m	Centimeter (cm) 0.01 m or $\frac{1}{100}$ m	Millimeter (mm) 0.001 m or $\frac{1}{1,000}$ m
10 × 1 hm	10 × 1 dam	10 × 1 m	10 × 1 dm	10 × 1 cm	10 × 1 mm	
	$\frac{1}{10}$ or 0.1 × 1 km	$\frac{1}{10}$ or 0.1 × 1 hm	$\frac{1}{10}$ or 0.1 × 1 dam	$\frac{1}{10}$ or 0.1 × 1 m	$\frac{1}{10}$ or 0.1 × 1 dm	$\frac{1}{10}$ or 0.1 × 1 cm

Liquid Volume

Kiloliter (kL) 1,000 L			LITER (L) 1 L			Milliliter (mL) 0.001 L or $\frac{1}{1,000}$ L

Mass

Kilogram (kg) 1,000 g			GRAM (g) 1 g			Milligram (mg) 0.001 g or $\frac{1}{1,000}$ g

Size of unit gets smaller. →

Relate Metric Units of Length, Liquid Volume, and Mass

1 cubic **decimeter** can hold 1 **liter**.
1 **liter** of water has a mass of 1 **kilogram**.

1 cubic **centimeter** can hold 1 **milliliter**.
1 **milliliter** of water has a mass of 1 **gram**.

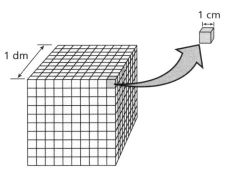

1 cm

1 dm

Examples of Metric Units

Length

1 kilometer (km)	1 hectometer (hm)	1 dekameter (dam)	1 meter (m)
about the distance you could walk in 12 minutes 1 km = 1,000 m	about the length of a football field 1 hm = 100 m	about the length of a school bus 1 dam = 10 m	about the distance from the floor to the doorknob

1 decimeter (dm)	1 centimeter (cm)	1 millimeter (mm)
about the length of a new crayon 10 dm = 1 m	about the width of your finger 100 cm = 1 m	about the thickness of a dime 1,000 mm = 1 m

Examples of Metric Units

Liquid Volume

1 kiloliter (kL)	1 liter (L)	1 milliliter (mL)
This cube holds 1 kiloliter of liquid.	This cube holds 1 liter of liquid.	This cube holds 1 milliliter of liquid.
1 kL = 1,000 L		1,000 mL = 1 L

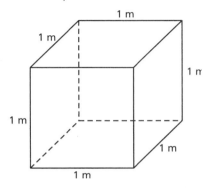
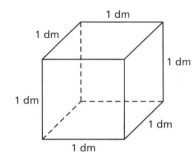
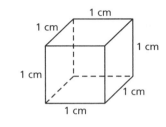

Mass

1 kilogram (kg)	1 gram (g)	1 milligram (mg)
about the mass of 5 bananas	about the mass of a paper clip	about the mass of a pinch of salt
1 kg = 1,000 g		1,000 mg = 1 g

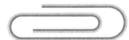

Customary Units

Length

	1 inch (in.)	1 Foot (ft)	1 Yard (yd)	1 Mile (mi)
in.		1 ft = 12 in.	1 yd = 36 in.	
ft	$\frac{1}{12}$ ft = 1 in.		1 yd = 3 ft	1 mi = 5,280 ft
yd	$\frac{1}{36}$ yd = 1 in.	$\frac{1}{3}$ yd = 1 ft		1 mi = 1,760 yd
mi		$\frac{1}{5,280}$ mi = 1 ft	$\frac{1}{1,760}$ mi = 1 yd	

Only commonly used conversions are given.

Liquid Volume

	1 Fluid Ounce (fl oz)	1 Cup (c)	1 Pint (pt)	1 Quart (qt)	1 Gallon (gal)
fl oz		1 c = 8 fl oz	1 pt = 16 fl oz	1 qt = 32 fl oz	1 gal = 128 fl oz
c	$\frac{1}{8}$ c = 1 fl oz		1 pt = 2 c	1 qt = 4 c	1 gal = 16 c
pt	$\frac{1}{16}$ pt = 1 fl oz	$\frac{1}{2}$ pt = 1 c		1 qt = 2 pt	
qt	$\frac{1}{32}$ qt = 1 fl oz	$\frac{1}{4}$ qt = 1 c	$\frac{1}{2}$ qt = 1 pt		1 gal = 4 qt
gal	$\frac{1}{128}$ gal = 1 fl oz	$\frac{1}{16}$ gal = 1 c		$\frac{1}{4}$ gal = 1 qt	

Only commonly used conversions are given.

Weight

	1 Ounce (oz)	1 Pound (lb)	1 Ton (T)
oz		1 lb = 16 oz	
lb	$\frac{1}{16}$ lb = 1 oz		1 T = 2,000 lb
T		$\frac{1}{2,000}$ T = 1 lb	

Only commonly used conversions are given.

Examples of Customary Units

Length

1 inch (in.)	1 foot (ft)	1 yard (yd)	1 mile (mi)
about the distance across a quarter	about the length of your math book 1 ft = 12 in.	about the length of a guitar 1 yd = 3 ft	about the distance you can walk in about 20 minutes 1 mi = 5,280 ft = 1,760 yd

Liquid Volume

1 cup (c)	1 pint (pt)	1 quart (qt)
1 c = 8 fluid ounces	1 pt = 2 c	1 qt = 2 pt = 4 c

1 half gallon ($\frac{1}{2}$ gal)	1 gallon (gal)
$\frac{1}{2}$ gal = 2 qt	1 gal = 4 qt

Customary Units

Examples of Customary Units

Weight

1 ounce (oz)	1 pound (lb)	1 ton (T)
about the weight of a slice of bread	about the weight of a package of butter 1 lb = 16 oz	about the weight of a small car 1 T = 2,000 lb

Table of Measures

Metric	Customary

Length/Area/Volume

Metric	Customary
1 millimeter (mm) = 0.001 meter (m)	1 foot (ft) = 12 inches (in.)
1 centimeter (cm) = 0.01 meter	1 yard (yd) = 36 inches
1 decimeter (dm) = 0.1 meter	1 yard = 3 feet
1 dekameter (dam) = 10 meters	1 mile (mi) = 5,280 feet
1 hectometer (hm) = 100 meters	1 mile = 1,760 yards
1 kilometer (km) = 1,000 meters	1 acre = 4,840 square yards
1 hectare (ha) = 1,000 square meters (m²)	1 acre = 43,560 square feet
1 square centimeter = 1 sq cm	1 acre = $\frac{1}{640}$ square mile
A metric unit for measuring area. It is the area of a square that is 1 centimeter on each side.	1 square inch = 1 sq in.
1 cubic centimeter = 1 cu cm	A customary unit for measuring area. It is the area of a square that is 1 inch on each side.
A unit for measuring volume. It is the volume of a cube with each edge 1 centimeter long.	1 cubic inch = 1 cu in.
	A unit for measuring volume. It is the volume of a cube with each edge 1 inch long.

Capacity

Metric	Customary
1 milliliter (mL) = 0.001 liter (L)	1 teaspoon (tsp) = $\frac{1}{6}$ fluid ounce (fl oz)
1 centiliter (cL) = 0.01 liter	1 tablespoon (tbsp) = $\frac{1}{2}$ fluid ounce
1 deciliter (dL) = 0.1 liter	1 cup (c) = 8 fluid ounces
1 dekaliter (daL) = 10 liters	1 pint (pt) = 2 cups
1 hectoliter (hL) = 100 liters	1 quart (qt) = 2 pints
1 kiloliter (kL) = 1,000 liters	1 gallon (gal) = 4 quarts

Mass / Weight

Mass	Weight
1 milligram (mg) = 0.001 gram (g)	1 pound (lb) = 16 ounces
1 centigram (cg) = 0.01 gram	1 ton (T) = 2,000 pounds
1 decigram (dg) = 0.1 gram	
1 dekagram (dag) = 10 grams	
1 hectogram (hg) = 100 grams	
1 kilogram (kg) = 1,000 grams	
1 metric ton = 1,000 kilograms	

Volume/Capacity/Mass for Water

1 cubic centimeter = 1 milliliter = 1 gram

1,000 cubic centimeters = 1 liter = 1 kilogram

Reference Tables

Table of Units of Time

Time

1 minute (min) = 60 seconds (sec)

1 hour (hr) = 60 minutes

1 day = 24 hours

1 week (wk) = 7 days

1 month is about 30 days

1 year (yr) = 12 months (mo)
or about 52 weeks

1 year = 365 days

1 leap year = 366 days

1 decade = 10 years

1 century = 100 years

1 millennium = 1,000 years

Table of Formulas

Perimeter

Polygon	P = sum of the lengths of the sides
Rectangle	$P = 2(l + w)$ or $P = 2l + 2w$
Square	$P = 4s$

Area

Rectangle	$A = l \cdot w$
Square	$A = s \cdot s$ or $A = s^2$

Volume of a Rectangular Prism

$$V = lwh \text{ or } V = Bh$$

(where B is the area of the base of the prism)

Properties of Operations

Associative Property of Addition

$(a + b) + c = a + (b + c)$	$(2 + 5) + 3 = 2 + (5 + 3)$

Commutative Property of Addition

$a + b = b + a$	$4 + 6 = 6 + 4$

Additive Identity Property of 0

$a + 0 = 0 + a = a$	$3 + 0 = 0 + 3 = 3$

Associative Property of Multiplication

$(a \cdot b) \cdot c = a \cdot (b \cdot c)$	$(3 \cdot 5) \cdot 7 = 3 \cdot (5 \cdot 7)$

Commutative Property of Multiplication

$a \cdot b = b \cdot a$	$6 \cdot 3 = 3 \cdot 6$

Multiplicative Identity Property of 1

$a \cdot 1 = 1 \cdot a = a$	$8 \cdot 1 = 1 \cdot 8 = 8$

Multiplicative Inverse

For every $a \neq 0$, there exists $\frac{1}{a}$ so that $a \cdot \frac{1}{a} = \frac{1}{a} \cdot a = 1$.

For $a = 5$, $5 \cdot \frac{1}{5} = \frac{1}{5} \cdot 5 = 1$.

Distributive Property of Multiplication over Addition

$a \cdot (b + c) = (a \cdot b) + (a \cdot c)$	$2 \cdot (4 + 3) = (2 \cdot 4) + (2 \cdot 3)$

Order of Operations

Step 1 Perform operations inside parentheses.

Step 2 Simplify powers.*

Step 3 Multiply and divide from left to right.

Step 4 Add and subtract from left to right.

*Grade 5 does not include simplifying expressions with exponents.

Problem Types

Addition and Subtraction Problem Types

	Result Unknown	Change Unknown	Start Unknown
Add to	A glass contained $\frac{2}{3}$ cup of orange juice. Then $\frac{1}{4}$ cup of pineapple juice was added. How much juice is in the glass now? *Situation and solution equation:*[1] $\frac{2}{3} + \frac{1}{4} = c$	A glass contained $\frac{2}{3}$ cup of orange juice. Then some pineapple juice was added. Now the glass contains $\frac{11}{12}$ cup of juice. How much pineapple juice was added? *Situation equation:* $\frac{2}{3} + c = \frac{11}{12}$ *Solution equation:* $c = \frac{11}{12} - \frac{2}{3}$	A glass contained some orange juice. Then $\frac{1}{4}$ cup of pineapple juice was added. Now the glass contains $\frac{11}{12}$ cup of juice. How much orange juice was in the glass to start? *Situation equation:* $c + \frac{1}{4} = \frac{11}{12}$ *Solution equation:* $c = \frac{11}{12} - \frac{1}{4}$
Take from	Micah had a ribbon $\frac{5}{6}$ yard long. He cut off a piece $\frac{1}{3}$ yard long. What is the length of the ribbon that is left? *Situation and solution equation:* $\frac{5}{6} - \frac{1}{3} = r$	Micah had a ribbon $\frac{5}{6}$ yard long. He cut off a piece. Now the ribbon is $\frac{1}{2}$ yard long. What is the length of the ribbon he cut off? *Situation equation:* $\frac{5}{6} - r = \frac{1}{2}$ *Solution equation:* $r = \frac{5}{6} - \frac{1}{2}$	Micah had a ribbon. He cut off a piece $\frac{1}{3}$ yard long. Now the ribbon is $\frac{1}{2}$ yard long. What was the length of the ribbon he started with? *Situation equation:* $r - \frac{1}{3} = \frac{1}{2}$ *Solution equation:* $r = \frac{1}{2} + \frac{1}{3}$

[1]A situation equation represents the structure (action) in the problem situation. A solution equation shows the operation used to find the answer.

Addition and Subtraction Problem Types (continued)

	Total Unknown	Addend Unknown	Other Addend Unknown
Put Together/ Take Apart	A baker combines $\frac{3}{4}$ cup of white flour and $\frac{1}{2}$ cup of wheat flour. How much flour is this altogether? *Math drawing:*[1] *Situation and solution equation:* $\frac{3}{4} + \frac{1}{2} = f$	Of the $1\frac{1}{4}$ cups of flour a baker uses, $\frac{3}{4}$ cup is white flour. The rest is wheat flour. How much wheat flour does the baker use? *Math drawing:* *Situation equation:* $1\frac{1}{4} = \frac{3}{4} + f$ *Solution equation:* $f = 1\frac{1}{4} - \frac{3}{4}$	A baker uses $1\frac{1}{4}$ cups of flour. Some is white flour and $\frac{1}{2}$ cup is wheat flour. How much white flour does the baker use? *Math drawing:* *Situation equation:* $1\frac{1}{4} = f + \frac{1}{2}$ *Solution equation:* $f = 1\frac{1}{4} - \frac{1}{2}$

Both Addends Unknown is a productive extension of this basic situation, especially for finding pairs of fractions with a given sum 1. Such take apart situations can be used to show all the decompositions of a given number. The associated equations, which have the total on the left of the equal sign, help students understand that the = sign does not always mean *makes* or *results in* but always does mean *is the same number as.*

Both Addends Unknown

A baker is making different kinds of bread using only the $\frac{1}{4}$ and $\frac{1}{2}$ cup measures. What different mixtures can be made with white flour and wheat flour to total $1\frac{1}{4}$ cups?

Math drawing:

Situation Equation:

$1\frac{1}{4} = f + h$

[1]These math drawings are called Math Mountains in Grades 1-3 and break-apart drawings in Grades 4 and 5.

Addition and Subtraction Problem Types

	Difference Unknown	Greater Unknown	Smaller Unknown
Additive Comparison[1]	**Using "More"** At a zoo, the female rhino weighs $1\frac{3}{4}$ tons. The male rhino weighs $2\frac{1}{2}$ tons. How much more does the male rhino weigh than the female rhino? **Using "Less"** At a zoo, the female rhino weighs $1\frac{3}{4}$ tons. The male rhino weighs $2\frac{1}{2}$ tons. How much less does the female rhino weigh than the male rhino? *Math drawing:* $2\frac{1}{2}$ $1\frac{3}{4}$ d *Situation equation:* $1\frac{3}{4} + d = 2\frac{1}{2}$ or $d = 2\frac{1}{2} - 1\frac{3}{4}$ *Solution equation:* $d = 2\frac{1}{2} - 1\frac{3}{4}$	**Leading Language** At a zoo, the female rhino weighs $1\frac{3}{4}$ tons. The male rhino weighs $\frac{3}{4}$ ton more than the female rhino. How much does the male rhino weigh? **Misleading Language** At a zoo, the female rhino weighs $1\frac{3}{4}$ tons. The female rhino weighs $\frac{3}{4}$ ton less than the male rhino. How much does the male rhino weigh? *Math drawing:* m $1\frac{3}{4}$ $\frac{3}{4}$ *Situation and solution equation:* $1\frac{3}{4} + \frac{3}{4} = m$	**Leading Language** At a zoo, the male rhino weighs $2\frac{1}{2}$ tons. The female rhino weighs $\frac{3}{4}$ ton less than the male rhino. How much does the female rhino weigh? **Misleading Language** At a zoo, the male rhino weighs $2\frac{1}{2}$ tons. The male rhino weighs $\frac{3}{4}$ ton more than the female rhino. How much does the female rhino weigh? *Math drawing:* $2\frac{1}{2}$ f $\frac{3}{4}$ *Situation equation:* $f + \frac{3}{4} = 2\frac{1}{2}$ or $f = 2\frac{1}{2} - \frac{3}{4}$ *Solution equation:* $f = 2\frac{1}{2} - \frac{3}{4}$

[1]A comparison sentence can always be said in two ways. One way uses *more,* and the other uses *fewer* or *less.* Misleading language suggests the wrong operation. For example, it says the *female rhino weighs $\frac{3}{4}$ ton less than the male,* but you have to add $\frac{3}{4}$ ton to the female's weight to get the male's weight.

Multiplication and Division Problem Types[1]

	Product Unknown	**Group Size Unknown**	**Number of Groups Unknown**
Equal Groups	Maddie ran around a $\frac{1}{4}$-mile track 16 times. How far did she run? *Situation and solution equation:* $n = 16 \cdot \frac{1}{4}$	Maddie ran around a track 16 times. She ran 4 miles in all. What is the distance around the track? *Situation equation:* $16 \cdot n = 4$ *Solution equation:* $n = 4 \div 16$	Maddie ran around a $\frac{1}{4}$-mile track. She ran a total distance of 4 miles. How many times did she run around the track? *Situation equation* $n \cdot \frac{1}{4} = 4$ *Solution equation:* $n = 4 \div \frac{1}{4}$

	Product Unknown	**Factor Unknown**	**Factor Unknown**
Arrays[2]	An auditorium has 58 rows with 32 seats in each row. How many seats are in the auditorium? *Math drawing:* 32 58 │ s *Situation and solution equation:* $s = 58 \cdot 32$	An auditorium has 58 rows with the same number of seats in each row. There are 1,856 seats in all. How many seats are in each row? *Math drawing:* s 58 │ 1,856 *Situation equation:* $58 \cdot s = 1,856$ *Solution equation:* $s = 1,856 \div 58$	The 1,856 seats in an auditorium are arranged in rows of 32. How many rows of seats are there? *Math drawing:* 32 s │ 1,856 *Situation equation* $s \cdot 32 = 1,856$ *Solution equation:* $s = 1,856 \div 32$

[1] In Grade 5, students solve three types of fraction division problems: 1) They divide two whole numbers in cases where the quotient is a fraction; 2) They divide a whole number by a unit fraction; 3) They divide a unit fraction by a whole number. Fraction division with non-unit fractions is introduced in Grade 6.

[2] We use rectangle models for both array and area problems in Grades 5 and 6 because the numbers in the problems are too large to represent with arrays.

Multiplication and Division Problem Types

	Product Unknown	**Factor Unknown**	**Factor Unknown**
Area	A poster has a length of 1.2 meters and a width of 0.7 meter. What is the area of the poster? *Math drawing:* 0.7 | A | (1.2) *Situation and solution equation:* $A = 1.2 \cdot 0.7$	A poster has an area of 0.84 square meters. The length of the poster is 1.2 meters. What is the width of the poster? *Math drawing:* 1.2 w | 0.84 *Situation equation:* $1.2 \cdot w = 0.84$ *Solution equation:* $w = 0.84 \div 1.2$	A poster has an area of 0.84 square meters. The width of the poster is 0.7 meter. What is the length of the poster? *Math drawing:* *l* 0.7 | 0.84 *Situation equation* $l \cdot 0.7 = 0.84$ *Solution equation:* $l = 0.84 \div 0.7$

Multiplier > 1: Larger Unknown	**Multiplier > 1: Smaller Unknown**	**Multiplier > 1: Multiplier Unknown**
Sam has 5 times as many goldfish as Brady has. Brady has 3 goldfish. How many goldfish does Sam have?	Sam has 5 times as many goldfish as Brady has. Sam has 15 goldfish. How many goldfish does Brady have?	Sam has 15 goldfish. Brady has 3 goldfish. The number of goldfish Sam has is how many times the number Brady has?

Multiplicative Comparison

Math drawing:

s | 3 : 3 : 3 : 3 : 3 |

b | 3 |

$b = s \div 5$ and $s = 5 \cdot b$

Situation and solution equation:
$s = 5 \cdot 3$

Math drawing:

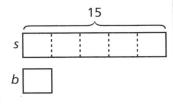

$b = s \div 5$ and $s = 5 \cdot b$

Situation equation:
$5 \cdot b = 15$

Solution equation:
$b = 15 \div 5$

Math drawing:

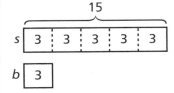

$b = s \div m$ and $s = m \cdot b$

Situation equation:
$15 = m \cdot 3$ or $3 = 15 \div m$

Solution equation:
$m = 15 \div 3$

Fractional Multiplier	**Fractional Multiplier**	**Fractional Multiplier**
Brady has $\frac{1}{5}$ times as many goldfish as Sam has. Sam has 15 goldfish. How many goldfish does Brady have?	Brady has $\frac{1}{5}$ times as many goldfish as Sam has. Brady has 3 goldfish. How many goldfish does Sam have?	Sam has 15 goldfish. Brady has 3 goldfish. The number of goldfish Brady has is how many times the number Sam has?

Math drawing:

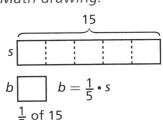

$b = \frac{1}{5} \cdot s$

$\frac{1}{5}$ of 15

Situation and solution equation:
$b = \frac{1}{5} \cdot 15$

Math drawing:

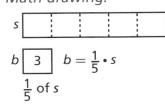

$b = \frac{1}{5} \cdot s$

$\frac{1}{5}$ of s

Situation equation:
$3 = \frac{1}{5} \cdot s$

Solution equation:
$s = 3 \div \frac{1}{5}$

Math drawing:

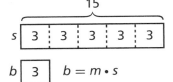

$b = m \cdot s$

Situation equation:
$3 = m \cdot 15$

Solution equation:
$m = 3 \div 15$

MathWord **Power**

Word Review

Work with a partner. Choose a word from a current unit or a review word from a previous unit. Use the word to complete one of the activities listed on the right. Then ask your partner if they have any edits to your work or questions about what you described. Repeat, having your partner choose a word.

Activities

- Give the meaning in words or gestures.
- Use the word in a sentence.
- Give another word that is related to the word in some way and explain the relationship.

Crossword Puzzle

Create a crossword puzzle similar to the example below. Use vocabulary words from the unit. You can add other related words, too. Challenge your partner to solve the puzzle.

Across

2. The answer to an addition problem
4. _____ and subtraction are inverse operations.
5. To put amounts together
6. When you trade 10 ones for 1 ten, you _____.

Down

1. The number to be divided in a division problem
2. The operation that you can use to find out how much more one number is than another
3. A fraction with a numerator of 1 is a _____ fraction.

The crossword puzzle is filled in as follows:

1 Down: division
2 Across: sum
2 Down: subtraction
3 Down: unit
4 Across: addition
5 Across: add
6 Across: group

Word Wall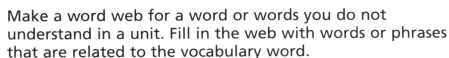

With your teacher's permission, start a word wall in your classroom. As you work through each lesson, put the math vocabulary words on index cards and place them on the word wall. You can work with a partner or a small group to choose a word and give the definition.

Word Web

Make a word web for a word or words you do not understand in a unit. Fill in the web with words or phrases that are related to the vocabulary word.

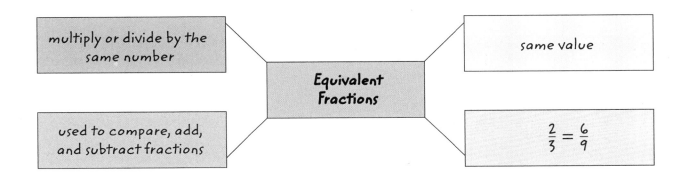

multiply or divide by the same number

same value

Equivalent Fractions

used to compare, add, and subtract fractions

$$\frac{2}{3} = \frac{6}{9}$$

Alphabet Challenge

Take an alphabet challenge. Choose three letters from the alphabet. Think of three vocabulary words for each letter. Then write the definition or draw an example for each word.

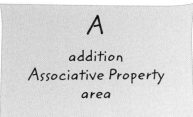

A

addition
Associative Property
area

E

exponent
expanded form
estimate

L

liter
line
line plot

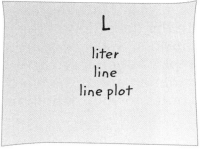

Vocabulary Activities

Concentration

Write the vocabulary words and related words from a unit on index cards. Write the definitions on a different set of index cards. Choose 3 to 6 pairs of vocabulary words and definitions. Mix up the set of pairs. Then place the cards facedown on a table. Take turns turning over two cards. If one card is a word and one card is a definition that matches the word, take the pair. Continue until each word has been matched with its definition.

area

The number of square units that cover a figure.

Math Journal

As you learn new words, write them in your Math Journal. Write the definition of the word and include a sketch or an example. As you learn new information about the word, add notes to your definition.

rectangular prism: a solid figure with two rectangular bases that are congruent and parallel

volume: a measure of the amount of space occupied by a solid figure

What's the Word?

Work together to make a poster or bulletin board display of the words in a unit. Write definitions on a set of index cards. Mix up the cards. Work with a partner, choosing a definition from the index cards. Have your partner point to the word on the poster and name the matching math vocabulary word. Switch roles and try the activity again.

a point of reference used for comparing and estimating

estimate

round

mixed number

equivalent fraction

common denominator

benchmark

simplify a fraction

unsimplify a fraction

unit fraction

Glossary

acute triangle
A triangle with three acute angles.

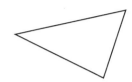

additive comparison
A comparison in which one quantity is an amount greater or less than another. An additive comparison can be represented by an addition equation or a subtraction equation.

Example:
Josh has 5 more goldfish than Tia.

$j = t + 5$

$j - 5 = t$

area
The number of unit squares that cover a two-dimensional figure without gaps or overlap.

Example:

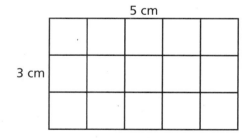

Area = 3 cm × 5 cm = 15 sq cm

Associative Property of Addition
Changing the grouping of addends does not change the sum. In symbols, $(a + b) + c = a + (b + c)$ for any numbers a, b, and c.

Example:
$(4.7 + 2.6) + 1.4 = 4.7 + (2.6 + 1.4)$

Associative Property of Multiplication
Changing the grouping of factors does not change the product. In symbols, $(a \cdot b) \cdot c = a \cdot (b \cdot c)$ for any numbers a, b, and c.

Example:
$(0.73 \cdot 0.2) \cdot 5 = 0.73 \cdot (0.2 \cdot 5)$

base
In a power, the number that is used as a repeated factor.

Example:
In the power 10^3, the base is 10.

base of a parallelogram
A side of a parallelogram that is perpendicular to its height.

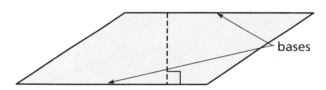

bases

base of a prism
One of two congruent parallel faces of a prism.

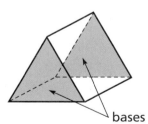

bases

base of a triangle
The side of a triangle that is perpendicular to its height.

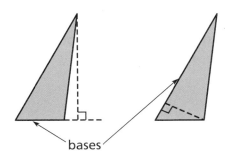
bases

benchmark
A point of reference used for comparing and estimating. The numbers 0, $\frac{1}{2}$, and 1 are common fraction benchmarks.

C

centimeter (cm)
A unit of length in the metric system that equals one hundredth of a meter. 1 cm = 0.01 m

closed shape
A shape that starts and ends at the same point.

common denominator
A common multiple of two or more denominators.

Example:
18 is a common denominator of $\frac{2}{3}$ and $\frac{5}{6}$.
$\frac{2}{3} = \frac{12}{18}$ and $\frac{5}{6} = \frac{15}{18}$

Commutative Property of Addition
Changing the order of addends does not change the sum. In symbols, $a + b = b + a$ for any numbers a and b.

Example:
$\frac{3}{5} + \frac{4}{9} = \frac{4}{9} + \frac{3}{5}$

Commutative Property of Multiplication
Changing the order of factors does not change the product. In symbols, $a \cdot b = b \cdot a$ for any numbers a and b.

Example:
$\frac{3}{7} \cdot \frac{4}{5} = \frac{4}{5} \cdot \frac{3}{7}$

comparison
A statement, model, or drawing that shows the relationship between two quantities.

comparison bars
Bars that represent the greater amount and the lesser amount in a comparison situation.

Example:
Sarah made 2 quarts of soup. Ryan made 6 quarts. These comparison bars show that Ryan made 3 times as many quarts as Sarah.

| Ryan (r) | 2 | 2 | 2 | 6 |
| Sarah (s) | 2 | | | |

complex figure
A figure made up of two or more basic shapes.

Example:
This figure is made up of a small rectangle and a large square.

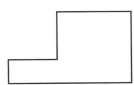

© Houghton Mifflin Harcourt Publishing Company

composite number
A whole number that has more than two factors.

Example:
The whole number 12 is a composite number because 1, 2, 3, 4, 6, and 12 are factors of 12.

composite solid
A solid figure made by combining two or more basic solid figures.

Example:
The composite solid on the left below is composed of two rectangular prisms, as shown on the right.

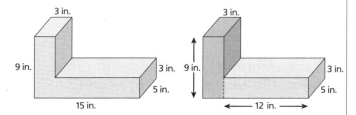

concave polygon
A polygon for which you can connect two points inside the polygon with a segment that passes outside the polygon. A concave polygon has a "dent."

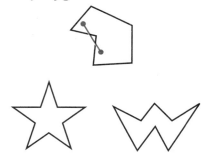

cone
A three-dimensional figure that has one flat base that is a circle.

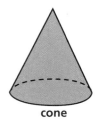

cone

congruent
Having the same size and shape.

convex polygon
A polygon that is not concave. All the inside angles of a convex polygon have a measure less than 180°.

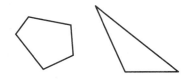

coordinate plane
A system of coordinates formed by the perpendicular intersection of horizontal and vertical number lines.

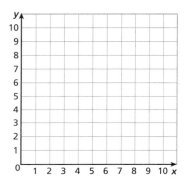

cube
A three-dimensional figure that is made of six square congruent faces.

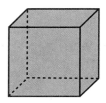

cubic unit
The volume of a unit cube. A cubic unit is a unit for measuring volume.

cylinder
A three-dimensional figure that has two flat, congruent bases that are circles.

cylinder

D

---

decimal
A number that includes a decimal point separating the whole number part of the number from the fraction part of the number.

Examples:

7.3	seven and three tenths
42.081	forty-two and eighty-one thousandths
0.72	seventy-two hundredths

decimeter (dm)
A unit of length in the metric system that equals one tenth of a meter.
1 dm = 0.1 m

Digit-by-Digit Method *
A method for solving division problems.

Example:

```
       546
   7) 3,822
     −35
     ─────
      32
     −28
     ─────
      42
     −42
```

dimensions
The length, width, or height of a figure.

Distributive Property of Multiplication over Addition
Multiplying a number by a sum gives the same result as multiplying the number by each addend and then adding the products. In symbols, for all numbers *a*, *b*, and *c*:
$$a \times (b + c) = a \times b + a \times c$$

Example:
$$4 \times (2 + 0.75) = 4 \times 2 + 4 \times 0.75$$

dividend
The number that is divided in a division problem.
Example:

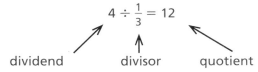

$$4 \div \frac{1}{3} = 12$$

dividend   divisor   quotient

divisor
The number you divide by in a division problem.
Example:

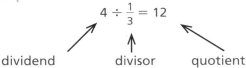

$$4 \div \frac{1}{3} = 12$$

dividend   divisor   quotient

double bar graph
A graph that uses vertical or horizontal bars to compare data for two groups.

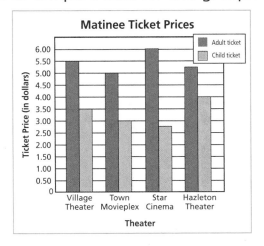

---

*A classroom research-based term developed for *Math Expressions*

Glossary

E

edge
A line segment where two faces of a three-dimensional figure meet.

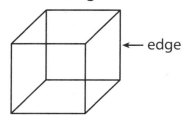

← edge

equilateral triangle
A triangle with three sides of the same length.

Example:

equivalent decimals
Decimals that represent the same value.

Example:
0.07 and 0.070 are equivalent decimals.

equivalent fractions
Fractions that represent the same value.

Example:
$\frac{1}{2}$ and $\frac{3}{6}$ are equivalent fractions.

estimate
Find *about* how many or *about* how much, often by using rounding or benchmarks.

evaluate
To substitute values for the variables in an expression and then simplify the resulting expression.

Example:
Evaluate $7 + 5 \cdot n$ for $n = 2$.

$7 + 5 \cdot n = 7 + 5 \cdot 2$ Substitute 2 for n.

$\qquad\quad = 7 + 10$ Multiply.

$\qquad\quad = 17$ Add.

expanded form
A way of writing a number that shows the value of each of its digits.

Example:
The expanded form of 35.026 is:

Using decimals:

$30 + 5 + 0.02 + 0.006$.

Using place values:
$(3 \times 10) + (5 \times 1) + (2 \times \frac{1}{100}) + (6 \times \frac{1}{1,000})$
or $(3 \times 10) + (5 \times 1) + (2 \times 0.01) + (6 \times 0.001)$.

Expanded Notation Method*
A method for solving multidigit multiplication and division problems.

Examples:

```
    43
  × 67
  2,400
    280
    180
     21
  2,881
```

```
          6
         40 ) 546
        500
    7) 3,822
     −3,500
        322
       −280
         42
        −42
```

exponent
In a power, the number that tells how many times the base is used as a factor.

Example:
In the power 10^3, the exponent is 3.
$10^3 = 10 \times 10 \times 10$

exponential form
The representation of a number that uses a base and an exponent.

Example:
The exponential form of 100 is 10^2.

© Houghton Mifflin Harcourt Publishing Company

*A classroom research-based term developed for *Math Expressions*

expression

A number, variable, or a combination of numbers and variables with one or more operations.

Examples:

4

t

$6 \cdot n$

$4 \div p + 5$

$5 \times 4 + 3 \times 7$

$6 \cdot (x + 2)$

F

face

A flat surface of a three-dimensional figure.

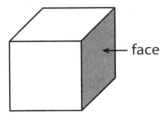

face

factor

One of two or more numbers multiplied to get a product.

Example:

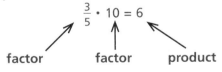

$$\frac{3}{5} \cdot 10 = 6$$

factor   factor   product

frequency table

A table that shows how many times each outcome, item, or category occurs.

Outcome	Number of Students
1	6
2	3
3	5
4	4
5	2
6	5

function

A relationship between two sets of numbers. Each number in one set is paired with exactly one number in the other set. A function can be described by an equation, a table of ordered pairs of numbers (an input/output table), a verbal rule, or a graph.

G

greater than ($>$)

A symbol used to show how two numbers compare. The greater number goes before the $>$ symbol and the lesser number goes after.

Example:

$\frac{2}{3} > \frac{1}{2}$ Two thirds is greater than one half.

H

height of a parallelogram

A measure of a line segment that is perpendicular to the base of the parallelogram.

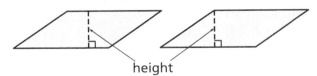

height

height of a triangle

The measure of a line segment that extends from a vertex to one side of the triangle (or an extension of that side) and forms a right angle with that side (or its extension).

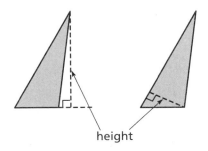

height

Glossary

hundredth
A unit fraction representing one of one hundred equal parts of a whole, written as 0.01 or $\frac{1}{100}$.

hypothesis
A statement used as a basis of an investigation.

Example:

Survey: Students' favorite breakfast foods

Possible hypothesis: Most students will choose pancakes as their favorite breakfast.

I

inequality
A mathematical sentence that contains > (is greater than), < (is less than), ≥ (is greater than or equal to), ≤ (is less than or equal to), or ≠ (is not equal to).

Examples:

$a > 5$
$14 \leq b + 3$

integers
All whole numbers (0, 1, 2, 3, …) and their opposites.
…, $^-3$, $^-2$, $^-1$, 0, $^+1$, $^+2$, $^+3$, …

isosceles triangle
A triangle with at least two sides of the same length.

Examples:

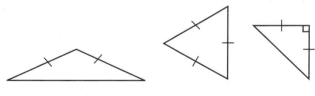

L

length
Measurement of how wide, tall, or long something is.

less than (<)
A symbol used to show how two numbers compare. The lesser number goes before the < symbol and the greater number goes after.

Example:
$\frac{1}{4} < \frac{1}{3}$ One fourth is less than one third.

line graph
A graph that uses a line or line segments to show how a quantity changes over time.

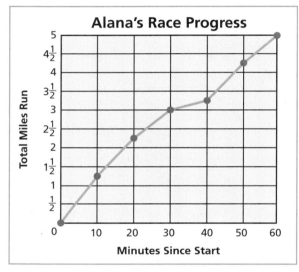

line plot
A diagram that uses a number line to show the frequency of data.

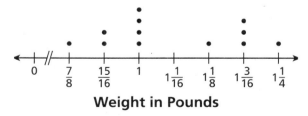

Weight in Pounds

M

mean
The sum of the values in a set of data divided by the number of values.

Glossary

median
The middle value when the values in a set of data are listed in order from least to greatest or greatest to least. When there are two middle values, the median is the mean of the two middle values.

meter (m)
The basic unit of length in the metric system.

mile (mi)
A U.S. customary unit of length equal to 5,280 feet or 1,760 yards.

millimeter (mm)
A unit of length in the metric system that equals one thousandth of a meter.
1 mm = 0.001 m

mixed number
A number with a whole number part and a fraction part.

Example:
The mixed number $3\frac{2}{5}$ means $3 + \frac{2}{5}$.

multiplicative comparison
A comparison in which one quantity is a number of times the size of another. A multiplicative comparison can be represented by a multiplication equation or a division equation.

Example:
Tomás picked 3 times as many apples as Catie.

$t = 3 \cdot c$
$t \div 3 = c$ or $\frac{1}{3} \cdot t = c$

multiplier
The number that another number is multiplied by. The number the numerator and denominator of a fraction are multiplied by to get an equivalent fraction can be called a multiplier.

Example:
A multiplier of 5 changes $\frac{2}{3}$ to $\frac{10}{15}$.

N

negative numbers
The numbers to the left of, or below, zero on a number line.

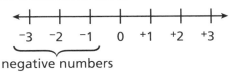

net
A flat or plane figure that can be cut and folded to form a three-dimensional figure.

New Groups Below Method*
A method used to solve multidigit multiplication problems.

Example:

```
      67
   ×  43
     1 2
      81
   2 2
     480
     1
   2,881
```

numerical pattern
A sequence of numbers that share a relationship.

Example:
In this numerical pattern, each term is 3 more than the term before.
2, 5, 8, 11, 14, . . .

O

obtuse triangle
A triangle with an obtuse angle.

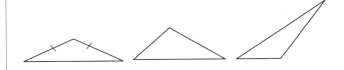

*A classroom research-based term developed for *Math Expressions*

Glossary

one-dimensional
Having a single dimension. Length is one-dimensional.

1 cm

open shape
A shape that does not start and end at the same point.

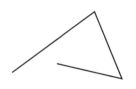

opposites
Two numbers that are the same distance from zero on a number line, but in opposite directions.

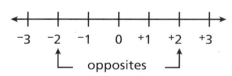

Order of Operations
A rule that states the order in which the operations in an expression should be done:

Step 1: Perform operations inside parentheses.

Step 2: Multiply and divide from left to right.

Step 3: Add and subtract from left to right.

ordered pair
A pair of numbers that shows the position of a point on a coordinate plane.

Example:
The ordered pair (3, 4) represents a point 3 units to the right of the *y*-axis and 4 units above the *x*-axis.

origin
The point (0, 0) on the coordinate plane.

overestimate
An estimate that is too big.

parallelogram
A quadrilateral with two pairs of parallel sides.

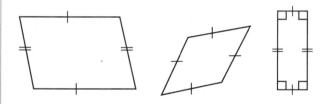

partial products
In a multidigit multiplication problem, the products obtained by multiplying each place value of one factor by each place value of the other.

Example:
In the problem below, the partial products are in red.

$25 \cdot 53 = 20 \cdot 50 + 20 \cdot 3 + 5 \cdot 50 + 5 \cdot 3$

percent
A way to represent a number *per hundred*. The symbol for percent is %.

Example:
$\frac{35}{100} = 35\%$

perimeter
The distance around a figure.

Example:
Perimeter = $2 \cdot 3$ cm + $2 \cdot 5$ cm = 16 cm

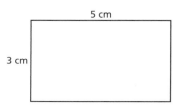
5 cm
3 cm

perpendicular
Two lines or line segments are perpendicular if they cross or meet to form 90° angles (square corners).

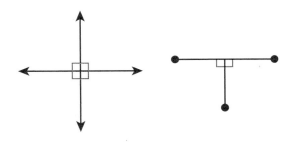

Place Value Rows Method*
A method used to solve multidigit multiplication problems.

Example:

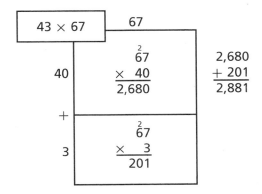

Place Value Sections Method*
A method used to solve multidigit multiplication and division problems.

Examples:

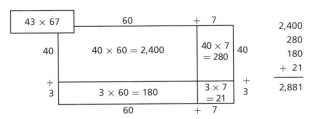

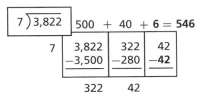

polygon
A closed two-dimensional shape made from line segments that do not cross each other.

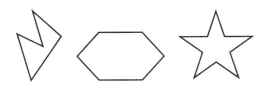

positive numbers
The numbers to the right of, or above, zero on a number line.

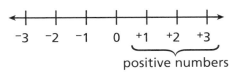

power of ten
A power with a base of 10. A number in the form 10^n.

Examples:
10^1, 10^2, 10^3

prism
A three-dimensional figure that has two congruent opposite faces that are polygons. The shape of the base is used to name the prism.

rectangular prism   pentagonal prism

product
The result of a multiplication.

Example:

$$\frac{3}{5} \cdot 10 = 6$$

factor   factor   product

*A classroom research-based term developed for *Math Expressions*

Glossary

pyramid
A three-dimensional figure that has a polygon-shaped base and triangular faces that meet at a point. The shape of the base is used to name the pyramid.

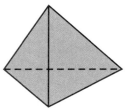 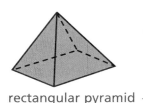

triangular pyramid   rectangular pyramid

Q

quadrilateral
A closed two-dimensional shape with four straight sides.

  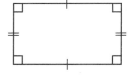

quotient
The answer to a division problem.

Example:

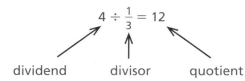

$$4 \div \frac{1}{3} = 12$$

dividend   divisor   quotient

R

range
The difference between the least (or minimum) value in a set of data and the greatest (or maximum) value.

rectangle
A parallelogram with four right angles.

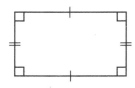 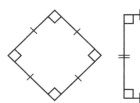

rectangular prism
A solid figure with two rectangular bases that are congruent and parallel.

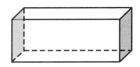

regular polygon
A polygon in which all sides and all angles are congruent.

 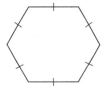

remainder
The number left over when a divisor does not divide evenly into a dividend.

Example:

$$7 \overline{)94} \quad \begin{array}{r} 13 \\ \hline \end{array}$$

```
      13
  7 )94
    -7
    ---
     24
    -21
    ---
      3  ←— remainder
```

rhombus
A parallelogram with four congruent sides.

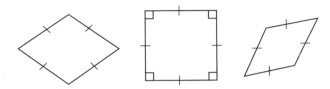

right triangle
A triangle with a right angle.

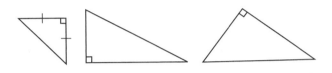

round
To change a number to a nearby number.

Examples:

54.72 rounded to the nearest ten is 50.

54.72 rounded to the nearest one is 55.

54.72 rounded to the nearest tenth is 54.7.

$3\frac{7}{9}$ rounded to the nearest whole number is 4.

S

scalene triangle
A triangle with no sides of the same length.

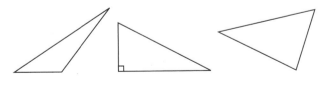

shift*
To change position. When we multiply a decimal or whole number by 10, 100, or 1,000, the digits shift to the left. When we divide by 10, 100, or 1,000, the digits shift to the right. When we multiply by 0.1, 0.01, or 0.001, the digits shift to the right. When we divide by 0.1, 0.01, or 0.001, the digits shift to the left.

Examples:

$72.4 \times 100 = 7{,}240$	Digits shift left 2 places.
$5.04 \div 10 = 0.504$	Digits shift right 1 place.
$729 \times 0.01 = 7.29$	Digits shift right 2 places.
$0.26 \div 0.001 = 260$	Digits shift left 3 places.

Short Cut Method*
A method used to solve multidigit multiplication problems.

Example:

$$
\begin{array}{r}
\overset{\overset{1}{2}}{43} \\
\times\ 67 \\
\hline
301 \\
2{,}580 \\
\hline
2{,}881
\end{array}
$$

simplify a fraction
To make an equivalent fraction by dividing the numerator and denominator of a fraction by the same number. Simplifying makes fewer but larger parts.

Example:
Simplify $\frac{12}{16}$ by dividing the numerator and denominator by 4.

$$\frac{12 \div 4}{16 \div 4} = \frac{3}{4}$$

simplify an expression
To use the Order of Operations to find the value of the expression.

Example:
Simplify $6 \cdot (2 + 5) \div 3$.

$$
\begin{aligned}
6 \cdot (2 + 5) \div 3 &= 6 \cdot 7 \div 3 \\
&= 42 \div 3 \\
&= 14
\end{aligned}
$$

*A classroom research-based term developed for *Math Expressions*

Glossary

situation equation*

An equation that shows the action or the relationship in a word problem.

Example:

Liam has some change in his pocket. He spends 25¢. Now he has 36¢ in his pocket. How much change did he have to start?

situation equation: $x - 25 = 36$

solution equation*

An equation that shows the operation to perform in order to solve a word problem.

Example:

Liam has some change in his pocket. He spends 25¢. Now he has 36¢ in his pocket. How much change did he have to start?

solution equation: $x = 36 + 25$

sphere

A three-dimensional figure made up of points that are the same distance from its center. It has no flat surfaces.

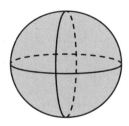

square

A rectangle with four congruent sides. (Or, a rhombus with four right angles.)

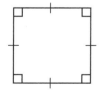 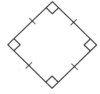

standard form

The form of a number using digits, in which the place of each digit indicates its value.

Example:

407.65

surface area

The total area of the faces or curved surfaces of a three-dimensional figure.

T

tenth

A unit fraction representing one of ten equal parts of a whole, written as 0.1 or $\frac{1}{10}$.

term

Each number in a numerical pattern.

Example:

In the pattern below, 3 is the first term, and 9 is the fourth term.

3, 5, 7, 9, 11, . . .

thousandth

A unit fraction representing one of one thousand equal parts of a whole, written as 0.001 or $\frac{1}{1,000}$.

three-dimensional

Having three dimensions, usually length, width, and height.

Volume

ton (T)

A U.S. customary unit of weight that equals 2,000 pounds.

*A classroom research-based term developed for *Math Expressions*

trapezoid
A quadrilateral with exactly one pair of parallel sides.

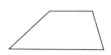

triangular prism
A three-dimensional figure that has two congruent parallel bases that are triangles.

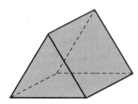

two-dimensional
Having two dimensions, usually length and width.

Area   1 cm   1 cm

U

underestimate
An estimate that is too small.

unit cube
A cube with side lengths of 1 unit.

1 unit   1 unit   1 unit

unit fraction
A fraction with a numerator of 1. A unit fraction is one of a number of equal sized parts that together make a whole.

Examples:
$\frac{1}{3}$ and $\frac{1}{12}$

unsimplify*
To make an equivalent fraction by multiplying the numerator and denominator of a fraction by the same number. Unsimplifying makes more but smaller parts.

Example:
Unsimplify $\frac{3}{4}$ by multiplying the numerator and denominator by 2.

$$\frac{3 \times 2}{4 \times 2} = \frac{6}{8}$$

V

variable
A letter or other symbol used to stand for an unknown number in an algebraic expression.

vertex (vertices)
In a two-dimensional figure, the point at which two line segments or two rays meet at an endpoint.

Example:
Line segments *RT* and *ST* meet at vertex *T*.

In a three-dimensional figure, the point at which three or more edges meet at a point.

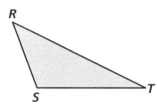 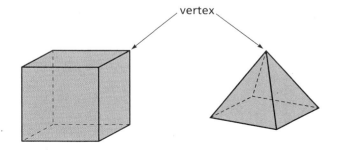

vertex

*A classroom research-based term developed for *Math Expressions*

Glossary

volume
A measure of the amount of space occupied by a solid figure. Volume is measured in cubic units.

W

word form
The form of a number that uses words instead of digits.

Example:
twelve and thirty-two hundredths

X

x-axis
The horizontal axis of the coordinate plane.

x-coordinate
The first number in an ordered pair, which represents a point's horizontal distance from the *y*-axis.

Example:
The *x*-coordinate of the point represented by the ordered pair (3, 4) is 3.

Y

y-axis
The vertical axis of the coordinate plane.

y-coordinate
The second number in an ordered pair, which represents a point's vertical distance from the *x*-axis.

Example:
The *y*-coordinate of the point represented by the ordered pair (3, 4) is 4.

5.ARO Algebraic Reasoning and Operations

5.ARO.1	Evaluate numerical expressions containing parentheses, brackets, or braces; use the symbols in numerical expressions.	Unit 1 Lessons 6, 12; Unit 2 Lessons 2, 7; Unit 3 Lessons 3, 7; Unit 4 Lesson 8; Unit 6 Lessons 8, 9, 10; Unit 7 Lessons 1, 3, 4, 7
5.ARO.2	Record numerical computation by writing simple expressions; explain the meaning of numerical expressions without evaluating them.	Unit 1 Lesson 1; Unit 6 Lessons 5, 8, 9, 10; Unit 7 Lessons 1, 2, 3, 4
5.ARO.3	Generate two numerical patterns using two given rules. Identify apparent relationships between corresponding terms. Form ordered pairs consisting of corresponding terms from the two patterns, and graph the ordered pairs on a coordinate plane.	Unit 7 Lessons 4, 6
5.ARO.3.a	Use positive and negative integers to describe quantities such as temperature above/below zero, elevation above/below sea level, or credit/debit.	Unit 7 Lesson 8
5.ARO.4	Form ordered pairs from a rule such as $y = 2x$, and graph the ordered pairs on a coordinate plane.	Unit 7 Lesson 6
5.ARO.5	Determine whether an equation or inequality involving a variable is true or false for a given value of the variable.	Unit 3 Lesson 14 Unit 7 Lesson 3
5.ARO.6	Represent real-world situations using equations and inequalities involving variables. Create real-world situations corresponding to equations and inequalities.	Unit 1, Lessons 6, 7, 9, 12; Unit 2 Lessons 4, 5, 6; Unit 3 Lessons 1, 3, 4, 5, 6, 7, 10, 11; Unit 4 Lessons 5, 8,11; Unit 5 Lesson 1; Unit 6 Lessons 1, 2, 3, 4, 5, 6, 7, 8, 9, 10; Unit 7 Lesson 3 Unit 8 Lesson 6

5.PVO Place Value and Operations

5.PVO.1	Understand that the value of a digit in a multi-digit whole number depends on its place in the number; know that each place is 10 times the value of the place to its *right* and $\frac{1}{10}$ the value of the place to its *left*.	Unit 2 Lessons 2, 3, 13; Unit 4 Lessons 1, 3, 7, 9
5.PVO.2	Understand the meaning of powers of 10. Recognize and explain patterns in the number of zeros in products of numbers multiplied by powers of 10. Given a decimal product or quotient, explain patterns in the position of the decimal point. Represent powers of 10 with whole number exponents.	Unit 4 Lessons 1, 2, 6, 7, 9; Unit 5 Lessons 6, 7, 8
5.PVO.3	Read and write decimals to millionths using base-ten numerals, number names, and expanded form. Compare and order decimals based on meanings of the digits in each place, using >, =, and < symbols to record the results of comparisons.	Unit 2 Lessons 1, 2, 3, 9, 10, 13, 14; Unit 4 Lesson 12; Unit 6 Lesson 11 Unit 7 Lesson 3; Unit 8 Lesson 9

5.PVO.4	Round decimals to any place applying place value understandings.	Unit 2 Lessons 8, 9; Unit 4 Lesson 10; Unit 6 Lesson 4
5.PVO.5	Use the standard algorithm to multiply multi-digit whole numbers, demonstrating fluency.	Unit 4 Lessons 3, 4, 5, 8, 10, 11, 12; Unit 6 Lessons 2, 6, 8, 9; Unit 8 Lessons 2, 6, 8, 11, 12, 17, 18, 20, 21
5.PVO.6	Use strategies involving place value, properties of operations, and/or the relationship between multiplication and division, to divide whole number dividends (through four digits) by two-digit divisors and express the quotients as whole numbers. Use equations, arrays, and/or area models to represent and explain the computation.	Unit 5 Lessons 1, 2, 3, 4, 5, 9, 10; Unit 6 Lessons 2, 4, 5, 7, 9, 10 Unit 7 Lesson 11; Unit 8 Lessons 2, 3, 6, 11, 12, 17, 19
5.PVO.7	Use diagrams or concrete models and strategies involving place value, properties of operations, and/or the relationship between addition and subtraction to add subtract, multiply or divide decimals through hundredths. Explain how the chosen strategy relates to a written method and describe the reasoning used.	Unit 2 Lessons 4, 5, 6, 7, 10; Unit 4 Lessons 1, 6, 7, 8, 9, 10, 11, 12; Unit 5 Lessons 6, 7, 8, 9, 10, 11; Unit 6 Lessons 1, 2, 3, 4, 6, 7, 8, 9, 11; Unit 7 Lessons 2, 3, 11; Unit 8 Lessons 1, 2, 3, 9, 10

5.FO Fractions and Operations

5.FO.1	Add and subtract fractions and mixed numbers that have different denominators by rewriting the given fractions as equivalent fractions that result in sums or differences with like denominators.	Unit 1 Lessons 2, 3, 4, 5, 7, 8, 9, 10, 11, 12, 13; Unit 2 Lessons 5, 10; Unit 3 Lessons 7, 8, 13; Unit 6 Lessons 1, 4, 7, 8, 10, 11; Unit 7 Lessons 2, 3; Unit 8 Lessons 3, 13
5.FO.1.a	Order fractions, including mixed numbers and improper fractions, and locate them on a number line.	Unit 1 Lessons 2, 4, 5, 13; Unit 2 Lesson 10; Unit 3 Lesson 8
5.FO.2	Use addition and subtraction to solve word problems involving fractions that relate to the same whole and have like and/or different denominators; represent the problem with models or equations. Use benchmark fractions and fraction number sense to estimate (using mental math) and to determine if the results are reasonable.	Unit 1 Lessons 1, 5, 6, 7, 8, 9, 10, 11, 12, 13; Unit 3 Lessons 7, 8, 13, 14; Unit 6 Lessons 1, 4, 7, 8, 9, 10; Unit 8 Lesson 3
5.FO.3	Given a fraction $\frac{a}{b}$, describe it as dividing the numerator by the denominator, $a \div b$. Solve word problems involving whole-number division that results in fraction or mixed-number answers; represent the problem with fraction models or equations.	Unit 3 Lessons 10, 11, 13, 14; Unit 5 Lesson 4; Unit 6 Lessons 4, 7, 11; Unit 8 Lesson 17

5.FO.4	Multiply a fraction or whole number by a fraction, through applying and extending prior understandings of multiplication.	Unit 3 Lessons 1, 2, 3, 4, 5, 6, 7, 8, 9, 10, 12, 13, 14; Unit 6 Lessons 2, 3, 5, 6, 7, 8, 10; Unit 7 Lessons 2, 3; Unit 8 Lessons 11, 13, 18, 20, 21
5.FO.4.a	Describe $(\frac{a}{b}) \times q$ as a parts of the whole q that has been separated into b equal parts. (example: $\frac{3}{6} \times 4 = \frac{12}{6}$ or 2); understand the process as the equivalent sequence of operations, $a \times q \div b$. (example: $3 \times 4 \div 6$)	Unit 3 Lessons 1, 2, 3, 4, 5, 6, 7, 10, 14; Unit 6 Lesson 3; Unit 8 Lesson 11
5.FO.4.b	Given a rectangle with side lengths in fractions of a unit, find the area of the figure by tiling it with unit squares that correspond to the correct unit-fraction side length; show that the area is the same when the side lengths are multiplied. Multiply side lengths given in fractional units to find the area of a rectangle; represent the product as a rectangular area.	Unit 3 Lessons 4, 6, 7, 9; Unit 6 Lessons 2, 3, 8; Unit 8 Lesson 3
5.FO.5	Describe multiplication as a form of scaling or resizing.	Unit 3 Lessons 1, 2, 4, 7, 9, 12, 13; Unit 4 Lesson 12; Unit 5 Lesson 10; Unit 6 Lessons 2, 6
5.FO.5.a	Without carrying out multiplication, compare the magnitude of the product to one of the factors, based on the size of the other factor. (example: the product 4×2 can be thought of as *4 is 2 times as large as 2* and the product $\frac{1}{5} \times 10$ can be thought of as $\frac{1}{5}$ *the size of 10*)	Unit 3 Lessons 7, 8, 9, 12, 13, 14; Unit 4 Lesson 12; Unit 5 Lesson 10; Unit 6 Lessons 2, 6; Unit 8 Lesson 3
5.FO.5.b	By interpreting multiplication as scaling, describe why multiplying a given number by a fraction greater than 1 results in a product greater than the given number and recognize that multiplying by whole numbers greater than 1 has been previously learned. Describe why multiplying a given number by a fraction less than 1 produces a result less than the given number. Understand the relationship between multiplying a fraction $\frac{a}{b}$ by 1 and the principle of equivalent fractions, $\frac{a}{b} = \frac{(n \times a)}{(n \times b)}$.	Unit 3 Lessons 1, 7, 9, 12; Unit 4 Lesson 12; Unit 5 Lesson 10; Unit 6 Lesson 6
5.FO.6	Multiply fractions and/or mixed numbers to solve real-world problems; represent the problems with models or equations.	Unit 3 Lessons 1, 2, 3, 4, 5, 6, 7, 8, 9, 12, 13, 14; Unit 6 Lessons 2, 6, 8, 9, 10; Unit 8 Lessons 2, 3, 11, 12
5.FO.7	Divide a unit fraction by a whole number, and a whole number by a unit fraction through applying and extending prior knowledge of division.	Unit 3 Lessons 10, 11, 12, 13; Unit 6 Lessons 2, 3, 5, 8, 11; Unit 8 Lesson 3

5.FO.7.a	Understand and explain the meaning of dividing unit fractions by non-zero whole numbers, and find their quotients.	Unit 3 Lessons 10, 11, 12, 13; Unit 6 Lessons 2, 3
5.FO.7.b	Understand and explain the meaning of dividing whole numbers by unit fractions, and find their quotients.	Unit 3 Lessons 10, 11, 12, 13 Unit 6 Lessons 2, 3, 10; Unit 7 Lesson 3; Unit 8 Lesson 3
5.FO.7.c	Divide unit fractions by non-zero whole numbers, and/or whole numbers by unit fractions to solve real-world problems; represent the problems with fraction models and equations.	Unit 3, Lessons 10, 11, 12, 13, 14; Unit 6, Lessons 2, 3, 5,
5.FO.8	Recognize and generate equivalent forms of commonly used fractions, decimals, and percents (e.g., halves, thirds, fourths, fifths, and tenths).	Unit 1 Lesson 13; Unit 2 Lessons 1, 11, 12

5.MDA Measurement and Data Analysis

5.MDA.1	Change standard units of measurements from larger to smaller units or smaller to larger (example: 2 m = 200 cm). Solve multi-step, real-world problems involving changing from one unit to another within the same system.	Unit 2 Lesson 4; Unit 5 Lesson 5; Unit 8 Lessons 1, 2, 9, 10, 11, 12
5.MDA.2	Display data involving measurements given in fractions of a unit (example: $\frac{1}{8}, \frac{1}{4}, \frac{1}{2}$) on a line plot. Use the data from line plots to solve problems involving operations with fractions.	Unit 1 Lesson 10; Unit 3 Lesson 13; Unit 8 Lesson 13
5.MDA.2.a	Use observations, surveys, and experiments to collect, represent, and interpret the data using tables (e.g., frequency charts) and bar graphs.	Unit 7 Lesson 10
5.MDA.2.b	Formulate questions that can be addressed with data and make predictions about the data.	Unit 7 Lesson 10
5.MDA.2.c	Know and use the definitions of the mean, median and range of a set of data. Understand that the mean is a "leveling out" of data.	Unit 6 Lesson 11; Unit 7 Lesson 11

5.MDA.2.d	Create and analyze double-bar graphs and line graphs by applying understanding of whole numbers, fractions and decimals.	Unit 7 Lesson 9
5.MDA.2.e	Represent and interpret data using appropriate scale.	Unit 6 Lesson 11; Unit 7 Lesson 9, 10
5.MDA.3	Understand that volume is an attribute of three-dimensional (solid) figures; know concepts for measuring volume.	Unit 8 Lessons 4, 5, 7, 17
5.MDA.3.a	Understand that a cube with 1-unit side length is called a *unit cube* and has a volume of one *cubic unit*; a unit cube can be used to measure volume.	Unit 8 Lessons 4, 5
5.MDA.3.b	Recognize that a three-dimensional (solid) figure that can be packed with *n* cubes without gaps or overlaps, has a volume of *n* cubic units.	Unit 8 Lessons 4, 5
5.MDA.4	Use counting and centimeter cubes, inch cubes, foot cubes, and non-standard units, to measure volume.	Unit 8 Lessons 4, 5, 6
5.MDA.5	Connect volume to multiplication and addition; solve real-world and other mathematical problems that involve volume.	Unit 8 Lessons 5, 6, 8, 17
5.MDA.5.a	Measure the volume of right rectangular prisms that have whole-number side-lengths by packing the figures with unit cubes; demonstrate that the volume is the same as multiplying the three side-lengths or by finding the product of the area of the base and the height of a figure. Given three factors, show that they can represent volume and the Associative Property.	Unit 8 Lessons 5, 6, 17
5.MDA.5.b	Solve real-world and other mathematical problems involving the volume of right rectangular prisms with whole number side lengths, by applying the formulas $V = l \times w \times h$ and $V = b \times h$.	Unit 8 Lessons 5, 6, 7, 8, 17
5.MDA.5.c	Understand the additive concept of volume measurement. Given a composite figure made up of two right rectangular prisms that do not overlap, find the volume by adding the volumes of the two parts; solve real-world problems applying this method.	Unit 8 Lessons 5, 6, 8
5.MDA.6	Develop and use formulas to determine the area of triangles, parallelograms and figures that can be decomposed into triangles.	Unit 8 Lesson 18, 19, 20, 21, 23
5.MDA.7	Use various tools and strategies to measure the surface area of objects that are shaped like rectangular prisms.	Unit 8 Lessons 22, 23

Mathematical Standards

5.GCP Geometry and the Coordinate Plane

5.GCP.1	Define the coordinate system in terms of two perpendicular number lines (*axes*) that intersect at the 0-point of each axis; understand that the intersection is a given point in the plane (the *origin*), and is located by an ordered pair of numbers called *coordinates*. Recognize that the first number in the ordered pair tells how far to move in the direction of the first axis, the second tells how far to move in the direction of the second axis, and the order of the coordinates correspond to the names of the two axes: the *x*-axis and the *x*-coordinate, the *y*-axis, and the *y*-coordinate.	Unit 7 Lessons 5, 6, 7
5.GCP.2	Graph points in the first quadrant of the coordinate plane to represent real-world and other mathematical problems; express the values of the points in terms of the problem context.	Unit 7 Lessons 6, 7
5.GCP.3	Recognize that in a given category of two-dimensional figures, attributes belonging to a category, also apply to subcategories.	Unit 8 Lessons 14, 15, 16
5.GCP.4	Use properties of figures to classify two-dimensional figures according to a hierarchy.	Unit 8 Lessons 14, 15, 16
5.GCP.5	Describe and classify three-dimensional figures including cubes, prisms and pyramids by the number of edges, faces or vertices as well as the types of faces.	Unit 8 Lessons 22, 23, 24
5.GCP.6	Identify cones, pyramids, spheres, and cylinders.	Unit 8 Lessons 22, 23, 24
5.GCP.7	Recognize and draw a net for a three-dimensional figure.	Unit 8 Lessons 22, 23, 24

MPP1

Problem Solving

Unit 1 Lessons 1, 5, 7, 8, 9, 12, 13;
Unit 2 Lessons 4, 6, 7, 8, 9, 10, 13;
Unit 3 Lessons 1, 2, 3, 4, 5, 6, 7, 8, 9, 10, 11, 12, 13, 14;
Unit 4 Lessons 1, 3, 6, 7, 8, 11, 12;
Unit 5 Lessons 1, 2, 4, 6, 7, 8, 9, 10, 11;
Unit 6 Lessons 1, 2, 4, 5, 6, 7, 8, 9, 10, 11; Unit 7 Lessons 3, 4, 6, 7, 9, 11;
Unit 8 Lessons 1, 2, 6, 8, 9, 10, 11, 12, 15, 17

MPP2

Abstract and Quantitative Reasoning

Unit 1 Lessons 1, 2, 3, 4, 5, 7, 8, 13;
Unit 2 Lessons 1, 2, 3, 4, 5, 8, 10, 11, 13;
Unit 3 Lessons 3, 4, 5, 6, 7, 8, 10, 11, 12, 14;
Unit 4 Lessons 1, 3, 7, 9, 10, 11, 12;
Unit 5 Lessons 1, 3, 7, 8, 9, 10, 11;
Unit 6 Lessons 1, 2, 3, 5, 6, 11;
Unit 7 Lessons 1, 3, 4, 5, 6, 7, 8, 10, 11;
Unit 8 Lessons 1, 2, 5, 11, 12, 17, 19, 20

MPP3

Use and Evaluate Logical Reasoning

Unit 1 Lessons 1, 2, 3, 4, 5, 6, 7, 8, 9, 10, 11, 12, 13;
Unit 2 Lessons 1, 2, 3, 4, 5, 6, 7, 8, 9, 10, 11, 12, 13, 14;
Unit 3 Lessons 1, 2, 3, 4, 5, 6, 7, 8, 9, 10, 11, 12, 13, 14;
Unit 4 Lessons 1, 2, 3, 4, 6, 7, 8, 9, 10, 11, 12;
Unit 5 Lessons 1, 2, 3, 4, 5, 6, 7, 8, 9, 10, 11;
Unit 6 Lessons 1, 2, 3, 4, 5, 6, 7, 8, 9, 10, 11;
Unit 7 Lessons 1, 2, 3, 4, 5, 6, 7, 8, 9;
Unit 8 Lessons 1, 2, 3, 4, 5, 6, 7, 8, 9, 10, 11, 12, 13, 14, 15, 16, 17, 18, 19, 20, 21, 22, 23, 24

MPP4

Mathematical Modeling

Unit 1 Lessons 1, 3, 5, 6, 7, 8, 9, 12, 13;
Unit 2 Lessons 4, 9, 10, 12, 13, 14;
Unit 3 Lessons 1, 2, 3, 4, 10, 1i, 14;
Unit 4 Lessons 1, 2, 3, 6, 12;
Unit 5 Lessons 1, 2, 6, 11;
Unit 6 Lessons 1, 2, 3, 4, 5, 6, 7, 8, 10, 11;
Unit 7 Lessons 3, 6, 7, 8, 9, 11;
Unit 8 Lessons 4, 5, 13, 15, 17, 18, 19, 20, 22, 23

Mathematical Processes and Practices

MPP5

Use Mathematical Tools

Unit 1 Lessons 1, 2, 3, 4, 5, 13;
Unit 2 Lessons 2, 3, 4, 6, 8, 10, 13;
Unit 3 Lessons 3, 4, 10, 11, 14;
Unit 4 Lessons 1, 12;
Unit 5 Lessons 6, 11;
Unit 6 Lessons 3, 11;
Unit 7 Lessons 5, 6, 7;
Unit 8 Lessons 4, 6, 13, 14, 15, 16, 17, 23

MPP6

Use Precise Mathematical Language

Unit 1 Lessons 1, 2, 3, 4, 5, 6, 7, 8, 9, 10, 11, 12, 13;
Unit 2 Lessons 1, 2, 3, 4, 5, 6, 7, 8, 9, 10, 11, 12, 13, 14;
Unit 3 Lessons 1, 2, 3, 4, 5, 6, 7, 8, 9, 10, 11, 12, 13, 14;
Unit 4 Lessons 1, 2, 3, 4, 5, 6, 7, 8, 9, 10, 11, 12;
Unit 5 Lessons 1, 2, 3, 4, 5, 6, 7, 8, 9, 10, 11;
Unit 6 Lessons 1, 2, 3, 4, 5, 6, 7, 8, 9, 10, 11;
Unit 7 Lessons 1, 2, 3, 4, 5, 6, 7, 8, 9, 10, 11;
Unit 8 Lessons 1, 2, 3, 4, 5, 6, 7, 8, 9, 10, 11, 12, 13, 14, 15, 16, 17, 18, 19, 20, 21, 22, 23, 24

MPP7

See Structure

Unit 1 Lessons 1, 2, 3, 4, 9, 10, 12, 13;
Unit 2 Lessons 1, 3, 4, 7, 10, 13, 14;
Unit 3 Lessons 1, 2, 4, 6, 7, 9, 10, 14;
Unit 4 Lessons 2, 4, 6, 7, 8, 9, 12;
Unit 5 Lessons 1, 6, 8, 9, 11;
Unit 6 Lessons 2, 4, 6, 7, 11;
Unit 7 Lessons 2, 4, 5, 7, 8;
Unit 8 Lessons 1, 4, 9, 11, 12, 14, 15, 16, 17, 22, 23, 24

MPP8

Generalize

Unit 1 Lessons 3, 4, 7, 8, 9, 10, 13;
Unit 2 Lessons 1, 2, 3, 7, 8, 10, 11, 12, 13;
Unit 3 Lessons 2, 3, 4, 6, 7, 9, 10, 13, 14;
Unit 4 Lessons 1, 2, 6, 7, 8, 9, 11, 12;
Unit 5 Lessons 1, 3, 6, 7, 10, 11;
Unit 6 Lessons 4, 6, 11;
Unit 7 Lessons 3, 4, 5, 7, 10;
Unit 8 Lessons 3, 8, 9, 10, 13, 17, 23, 24

© Houghton Mifflin Harcourt Publishing Company

Index

Index

Index

Be an Illustrator

Illustrator: Josh Brill

Did you ever try to use shapes to draw animals like the sugar glider on the cover?

Over the last 10 years Josh has been using geometric shapes to design his animals. His aim is to keep the animal drawings simple and use color to make them appealing.

Add some color to the sugar glider Josh drew. Then try drawing a cat or dog or some other animal using the shapes below.

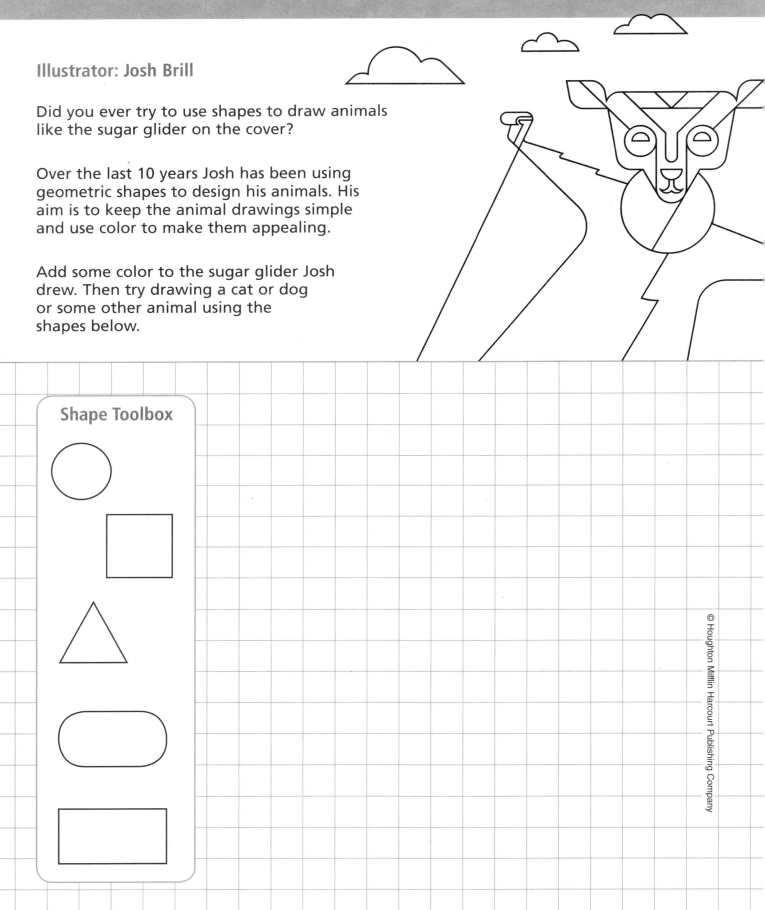

Shape Toolbox